SECOND EDITION

ELECTRICIANS GUIDE TO CONDUIT BENDING

D0943501

RICHARD A. COX
Journeyman Electrician (Wireman) I.B.E.W. Local 73
Chairman Electrical/Robotic Department
Spokane Community College
A.A.S. Occupational Education

 **PEND OREILLE PUBLICATIONS**

(Pond O Ray)

Box 3822 Spokane, Washington 99220

i

ELECTRICIANS
GUIDE TO CONDUIT BENDING

Special thanks to the following companies who furnished photographs, diagrams and/or technical data.

Allied Tube & Conduit Corp.
Harvey, Illinois

Enerpac
Butler, Wisconsin

Greenlee Tool Co.
Rockford, Illinois

Lindseen of North Carolina Inc.
Hayesville, North Carolina

Thermotools Co.
Cleveland, Ohio

Printed and bound in the United States of America
Ross Printing Company
Spokane, Washington 99220

To my devoted wife
PATRICIA
whose understanding
and help made
this book possible

INTRODUCTION

The purpose of this text is to assist the reader (Apprentice or Journeyman) with developing the techniques required to accurately and efficiently bend conduit.

Exposed conduit work is one area of an electrician's job that puts his skill on display. Exposed conduit is there for all to see and directly reflects on the ability of the installer. With these thoughts in mind, it then will benefit all electricians to learn one of several methods of bending conduit that will assure accurate, and precision bent conduit. Conduit that you can step back and look at with pride, and the knowledge that it was bent right the first time.

The formula methods that the text will deal with at first will seem slow and time consuming, but as you learn the method and become confident with the bender and your own abilities, it will be quicker and less time consuming than any other "ABOUT" methods in use by many electricians in the field today.

Some explanations of mathematical or trigonometric function have been over simplified so the reader may understand the principles and relationships without an extensive math background.

Terms and terminology used in the text, as with any trade, may be regional. A "WOW" in Chicago, Ill., may be a "HOOP-DE-DO" in Butte, Mont. For this reason, a complete glossary of terms is included with definitions. The reader, therefore, need only pick the definition that fits the term used in your area and the text will be understandable.

The text will lead you through the steps of procedure for formulated bending, and then let you apply what you have read with sample problems. The correct answers will be found at the back of the book. It is intended that these sample problems will enable the reader to gain confidence in the system and himself/herself.

For the best understanding of the material, read the chapters in order. Reference is made back to preceding chapters as to the methods and techniques and continuity will be lost if you attempt to "skip around".

It should be stated that with few exceptions, the methods and procedures outlined in this text are not original with the author, but are a culmination of ideas, techniques, and methods of many fine electricians from throughout the United States and Canada, men I had the pleasure of working with and sharing ideas on conduit bending. Although I would like to give individual credit, the list is too innumerable and I will simply say "THANK YOU" to those involved.

R.A.C.

"It is difficult to climb the ladder of success with your hands in your pockets."

Author unknown

TABLE OF CONTENTS

v

BASIC TRIGONOMETRY 1

A very basic understanding of trigonometry is needed to fully understand and appreciate formula conduit bending. Once the basic relationships of the right triangle are understood, the serious student of conduit bending can then fully understand "HOW AND WHY" the methods work, and will be able to develop his/her own formulas or tricks to make the job easier.

RIGHT TRIANGLES

A right triangle is a triangle in which one angle is a right angle (90°) and the other two angles, if added together, also total 90°, for a total sum of 180° for three angles (Fig. 1).

Fig. 1

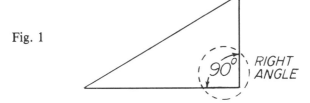

Of the two angles remaining in the triangle, one is called Angle Theta (Θ) and is used as a reference to identify the other sides of the triangle (Fig. 2).

Fig. 2

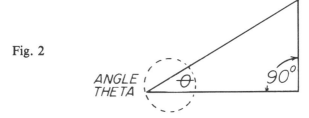

The side opposite Angle Theta (Θ) is called, the Opposite side (Fig. 3).

Fig. 3

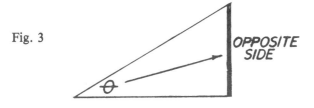

The side of the triangle next to (adjacent) angle Θ is called the Adjacent side (Fig. 4).

Fig. 4

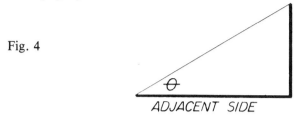

ADJACENT SIDE

The remaining side of the triangle which is opposite the right angle, is called the Hypotenuse (Fig. 5).

Fig. 5

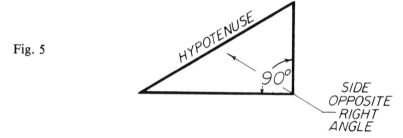

Mathematicians have been impressing layman with strange sounding terms for a long time. Even though the terms are strange sounding, they should not cause panic. Three such alien terms are: Sine, Cosine and Tangent. These terms quite simply are numerical constants for given angles. These numerical values are found in the Trigonometric (Trig) Function Chart located in the back of the book.

These constants (sine, cosine and tangent) have a fixed relationship with the sides and angle Theta of the right triangle. These ratios may be stated in formulas:

Sine of angle Θ $= \dfrac{O}{H}$

Cosine of angle Θ $= \dfrac{A}{H}$

Tangent of angle Θ $= \dfrac{O}{A}$

O = Opposite side
H = Hypotenuse
A = Adjacent

By using one or more of the formulas, we can find any side of a right triangle or angle Theta when the dimensions of two sides are known.

As with any formula of this type, two values must be known to find the third or unknown value. Using the formula Sine $= \dfrac{O}{H}$ as an example:

2

If the Sine of the angle is known, and the Hypotenuse is known, only the Opposite and Adjacent sides remain to be found. To find the Opposite side, the orignal formula Sine $= \dfrac{O}{H}$ would have to be transposed algebraically.

By placing formulas in so-called "MAGIC CIRCLES," they are easier to handle and transposition is not necessary, greatly simplifying the math.

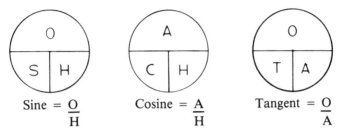

Sine $= \dfrac{O}{H}$ Cosine $= \dfrac{A}{H}$ Tangent $= \dfrac{O}{A}$

To use the magic circle, simply place the thumb or forefinger over the unknown value (Opposite side) and the circle tells you to multiply the sine of the angle by the Hypotenuse to find the Opposite side.

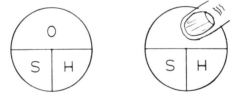

Had we known the Hypotenuse and the Opposite side and wanted to find the Sine, we would cover the unknown (Sine) and the circle tells us to divide the Opposite side by the Hypotenuse to find the Sine of the angle (Fig. 6).

Fig. 6

This is a very basic presentation of Trigonometric functions, but should be adequate enough to understand the relationship that exists between the Opposite side, Adjacent side, Hypotenuse and Angle Theta. Reference will be made throughout the text to these relationships and if you can understand the relationships you will be able to develop your own formulas or use Trig functions not only to

3

determine where bend(s) must be made, but also the degree of bend(s) for a given project.

Let's try some problems and see how it works.

PROBLEM: Assuming we want to bend a piece of conduit at 24'' and want it to raise 8''. What degree of bend will be required?

1. First draw the problem (Fig.7).

Fig. 7

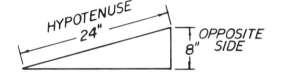

2. Look at it now as a right triangle, redraw and label (Fig. 8).

Fig. 8

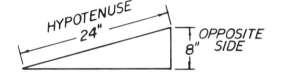

3. Select a formula that has the two known values (Hypotenuse and Opposite side). The Sine formula meets our needs.

4. Replace letters with number measurements from the problem and divide as indicated in the formula.

$$\text{Sine} = \frac{8}{24} \qquad \text{Sine} = .333$$

5. Turn to the Trigonometric Chart and find the angle that has a Sine of .333 or as close as possible. The closest angle is 19 degrees.

We could now bend the pipe using a protractor level or other device 19° and get the desired rise and length. In reality we would not go to all this trouble for such a simple bend, (a quick method is described later in the text) but did so only to try out the formulas. It was not all wasted motion, however, for this is the procedure to determine rate of rise of conduit.

The ratio of the sides of the triangle to a given angle Ɵ remain constant, even if the size of the triangle is increased (Fig. 9).

Fig. 9

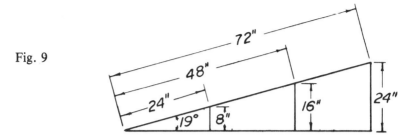

Notice that if the Hypotenuse doubles in length from the original dimensions, the Opposite side also doubles in length but angle Ɵ remained unchanged.

Sine Ɵ = $\frac{O}{H}$ Sine = $\frac{16}{48}$ Sine = .333

Sine of .333 is 19°

If the Hypotenuse is tripled in length, the Opposite side also triples, yet angle Ɵ remains the same.

Sine Ɵ = $\frac{O}{H}$ Sine = $\frac{24}{72}$ Sine = .333

Sine of .333 is 19°

This ratio will hold true no matter how large the triangle may become.

So in a practical sense, we could say that if we bend our conduit 19° at 24" it will rise 8" or a rate of rise of 4" per foot of length. If a 10 foot section of pipe were added, we know the rise would increase 4" X 10 or 40." Add this to the original 8" rise for a total of 48" (Fig. 9a).

Fig. 9a

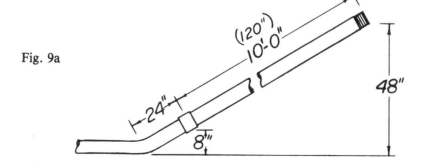

To prove our figures and check the rise again, let's use the formula.

$$\text{Sine} = \frac{O}{H}$$

We know the angle of bend is 19° and the Hypotenuse is now 24" + 120" or 144" total. The unknown then would be the Opposite side. Covering the Opposite side in the magic circle, tells us to multiply the Sine by the Hypotenuse.

$$O = .333 \times 144 \quad O = 47.952 \text{ or } 48''*$$

PROBLEM: A pipe must be bent at 44" and have a rise of 13". What angle of bend will be required?

Draw and label as a right triangle.

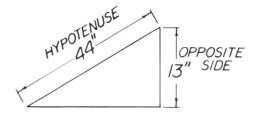

Using formula $S = \dfrac{O}{H}$

Substitute values $S = \dfrac{13}{44}$

Solve: Sine = .2954

From the Trigonometric Chart find the angle with a Sine of .2954

Answer 17°

---

*The small error is caused by selecting the closest degree at the beginning of the problem. A more accurate method would be to break degrees into minutes. But this is not necessary as we can only expect accuracy in conduit bending to be within 1/8" or .12500.

PROBLEMS:

1. How far will a pipe raise if it is bent 30° at 48''? What is the rise per foot?

2. An electrician has bent a piece of pipe as shown, what is the angle of bend A?

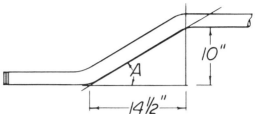

3. A guy wire 100 ft. long is attached at the top of a pole and secured to the ground 40 ft. from the base of the pole. What angle does the wire make with the ground? How tall is the pole?

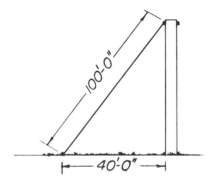

4. At what angle must a pipe be bent in order to make a 7 ft. rise in a 3 ft. horizontal distance?

Another method of solving problems dealing with right triangles and not requiring the unknown angle, is the Pythagorean Theory (developed over 2,500 years ago by a Greek scholar named Pythagoras). Pythagoras found that square areas of the two legs of a right triangle (Adjacent and Opposite) when added together, exactly equal the square area erected on the Hypotenuse (Fig. 10).

7

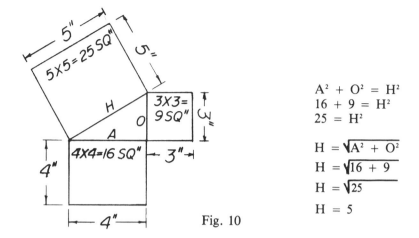

$$A^2 + O^2 = H^2$$
$$16 + 9 = H^2$$
$$25 = H^2$$

$$H = \sqrt{A^2 + O^2}$$
$$H = \sqrt{16 + 9}$$
$$H = \sqrt{25}$$
$$H = 5$$

Fig. 10

The theorem simply stated, gives us the formula $A^2 + O^2 = H^2$. Transposed, this forumla may also be stated

$$H = \sqrt{A^2 + O^2}$$

A formula very difficult to do long hand, but can be quickly completed on a pocket calculator.

ELECTRICAL METALLIC CONDUIT 2

Electrical Metallic Conduit is also referred to as "EMT" (Electrical Metallic Tubing), "STEEL TUBE" and "THIN WALL."

National Electrical Code® rules governing its use and installation are covered by NEC Article 348.

Standard EMT trade sizes are: ½", ¾", 1", 1¼", 1½", 2", 2½", 3" and 4" and are manufactured in 10 foot lengths.

Bending qualities will be effected by the ductility, uniformity and surface treatment of the conduit and these qualities will vary with the manufacturer.

Bending EMT

EMT may be bent with hand benders, "CHICAGO" type benders, electric or hydraulic benders.

Hand bending is usually restricted to ½", ¾", 1" and 1¼" pipe sizes. Over 1¼" conduit would require physical strength not possessed by most electricians.

"CHICAGO" benders vary with the manufacturer, but most will bend up to 2" EMT.

Hydraulic benders normally bend up to 2" pipe size. The Enerpac Co., however, has a bender ("EEGOR") that will bend EMT up through 4" trade size.

Only hand bending techniques will be discussed for EMT. "CHICAGO" and hydraulic methods are covered under rigid conduit and the techniques as outlined, will also apply to EMT.

HAND BENDERS: Hand Benders are offered by many manufacturers but are all basically the same (Fig. 11).

Fig. 11

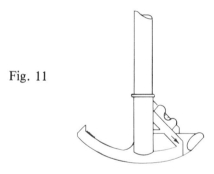

Each manufacturer puts marks, arrows, stars or whatever, on the bending shoe to locate center of bend, make adjustment for back-to-back bends, indicate starting point for 90° stub, etc. Take the time to read the instructions that come with each bending head. If no literature is available, make some sample bends with scrap pipe to familiarize yourself with the bender and its marks. The time will be well spent and pay dividends in time and material saved when the actual bending is started.

Some manufacturers also indicate that their benders can be used to bend the next smaller size Rigid pipe, i.e. 1" EMT/¾" Rigid. The author's experience has been that some Rigid Conduit is too hard and will distort the bending shoe and ruin the bender. The bender can also be ruined by loaning the bender to an Iron Worker to bend re-bar and both practices should be avoided whenever possible.

Benders do not come with a handle. The handle is cut from standard size Rigid or IMC Conduit and screwed into the bender head. To save back strain and to gain mechanical advantage, the bender handle should reach the elbow of the user when stood upright on the floor next to the body.

If your bender is not equipped with a 45° bubble, a 45° bend has been achieved on most benders when the handle of the bender is vertical or perpendicular to the work surface (Fig. 12).

Fig. 12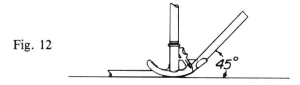

The key to accurate bending with a hand bender is constant foot pressure on the back piece. Failure to keep weight on the back piece will allow the conduit to raise off the floor and bend outside the bending shoe.

Proper body positioning when bending conduit will give added leverage and make the job easier.

Fig. 13 shows proper stance for initial bending of a 90° bend. Hold this position pulling the handle back toward the chest until the bender handle is just past vertical. Change body positioning, spacing feet further apart. The bend can now be completed by pushing down on the bender handle as shown in Fig. 14.

Fig. 13   Fig. 14

10

When it is necessary to invert the bender to complete some bends, constant pressure as close to the shoe as practicable must be applied with the hands to keep the conduit firmly in the bending shoe. This will ensure a true and proper bend (Fig. 15).

Fig. 15

NINETY DEGREE BENDS   3

Ninety degree bends are called "stubs." The measurement of a stub is taken from the back of the completed bend to the end of the pipe (Fig. 16).

Fig. 16

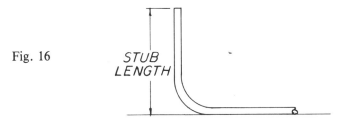

STUB
LENGTH

This is the most frequent bend the electrician will make and also one of the easiest. To bend stubs to a given dimension, the "take-up" of the bender must be known.

"Take-up" is the distance from the arrow (or other indicating mark used for bending 90°) on the bender to the back of the completed bend (Fig. 17). This distance remains constant for a given bender and once found can be used to accurately layout and bend 90° stubs.

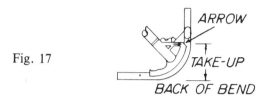

Fig. 17

Finding Bender Take-Up

To find the take-up or to check the take-up printed on the bender, proceed as follows:

1. Mark a scrap piece of pipe at 6".

2. Place the arrow (star or other mark) of the bender on the 6" mark as shown in Fig. 18a and bend a full 90° bend. Accuracy at this point is important so check your bend with a level.

3. Measure the over-all stub length and deduct 6", the remainder is "take-up" (Fig. 18b).

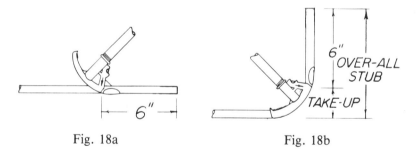

Fig. 18a   Fig. 18b

"Take-up" then is the measurement from the arrow to the back of the bend. This measurement remains the same and can be used to pre-measure 90° stubs.

EXAMPLE: Using a ½" bender with 5" take-up, we need to bend a 12" stub. Subtract the 5" take-up from 12", leaving 7". Mark the pipe 7" from the end. Place the arrow of the bender on the mark (Fig. 19) and bend 90°.

Fig. 19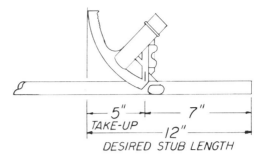

$$5" \quad\quad 7"$$
TAKE-UP
$$12"$$
DESIRED STUB LENGTH

RULE: When bending stubs using the take-up method, the bender is always placed on the pipe and the bend is made facing the end of the pipe the measurements were taken from.

In embedded or underground conduit work where accuracy and appearance is not so important, a quick method for bending 90° stubs is by sighting the back of the bender. Notice in Fig. 19 that the back of the bending shoe lines up with the 12" measurement for the desired stub length. If a 12" stub is required, measure 12" from end of conduit and place thumb to indicate mark. Place bender on conduit and sight back of bending shoe. Move conduit until back of shoe is lined up with thumb mark. Set bender and bend 90°. This is an "about" method and should not be used for exposed conduit runs.

TIP: Once the length of the stub has been determined, deduct take-up in your head to find bend mark. Do not mark pipe. Instead, place bender on pipe in approximate area where mark should be. Supporting the conduit in the bender with one hand, hook the end of a steel tape over end of conduit and then slide the bender until arrow of bender is on proper measurement (Fig. 20). Set bender and bend 90°. This eliminates fumbling for a pencil and saves time.

Fig. 20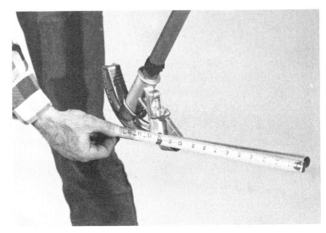

13

To straighten a stub that has been over-bent or to remove the bend completely, place bender handle (or any close fitting pipe) over the stub as shown in Fig. 21, and push down and away in one full motion. For larger sizes of EMT, a close fitting pipe that will fit inside will also work.

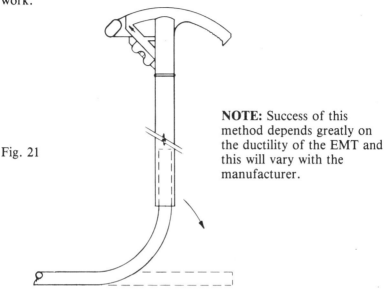

Fig. 21

NOTE: Success of this method depends greatly on the ductility of the EMT and this will vary with the manufacturer.

BACK-TO-BACK 90° BENDS　　　4

For making "back-to-back" or "U" bends, bend the first bend in the usual manner. To make the second bend, measure required distance between stubs from the back of the first bend. Deduct take-up and bend second 90° stub as shown in Fig. 22. If the pipe is too short and the bender must be reversed, an amount must now be added to the desired stub length mark (Fig. 23).

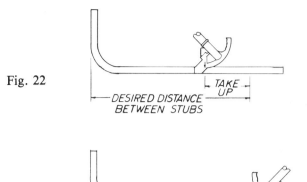

Fig. 22

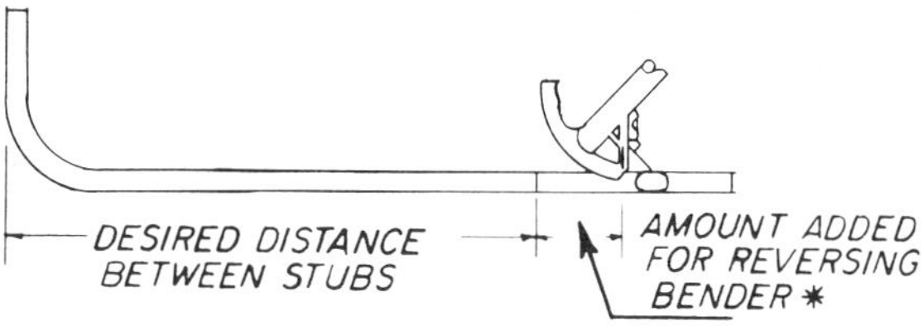

DESIRED DISTANCE
BETWEEN STUBS

TAKE UP

Fig. 23

DESIRED DISTANCE
BETWEEN STUBS

AMOUNT ADDED
FOR REVERSING
BENDER *

Most benders have a mark that may be used when bending back-to-back bends (some benders have the amount that must be added, printed on the bender head).

If your bender has no marks or information, bend a scrap piece of pipe to find the amount that must be added.

To determine the amount that must be added for reversing the bender, bend an 8" or 10" stub in a scrap piece of pipe. Using the bender handle as a straight edge, measure over 24" and place a mark on the conduit (Fig. 24).

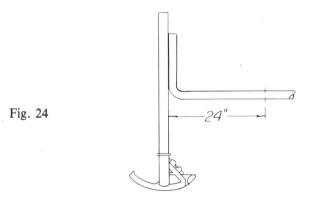

Fig. 24

24"

*As written on bender or as determined by trial bend.

15

Reverse bender (your back is to the first stub) and bend another 90° bend. Measure the back to back or outside to outside dimension of the two 90° bends. The measurement will be less than 24'', and the difference is the amount that must be added to the desired measurement for accurate back to back bends. The amount that must be added will vary with each pipe size and bender used.

TIP: When bending stubs, if you must turn your back on the end of the conduit you measured from to bend the second bend, you must ADD to the desired dimension, DO NOT subtract take-up.

KICKS   5

The term "KICK" is applied to any bend of less than 90°. Its primary use is for direction changes and works exceptionally well for entry into boxes and/or cabinets as shown in Fig. 25.

Fig. 25

The degree of bend for a given amount of kick will depend on bender placement on the conduit. Bending close to 90° stub requires more angle of bend for a given height (Fig. 26a), bending farther away from the stub requires less angle of bend (Fig. 26b).

Fig. 26a  Fig. 26b

45°   8"   15°

Installation requirements will dictate where conduit is to be "kicked."
The easiest method of bending kicks to a required measurement is to place conduit in bender and level 90° stub on a horizontal plane (Fig. 27). Holding the rule next to stub, read the measurement to the top of the pipe. Mentally add the amount of desired kick to this measurement and bend until stub has reached required height on the rule (Fig. 28).

Fig. 27

Fig. 28

OFFSETS 6

An offset is two bends placed in a piece of conduit to change elevation to go over or under obstructions or for proper entry in boxes, cabinets, etc.

Perfectly fitting offsets can be easily and quickly made, if first a few basic rules are learned and understood.

An offset consists of two bends having the same degree of bend. Fig. 29.

Fig. 29

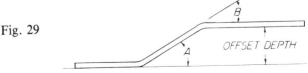

17

The degree of bend is dictated by space requirements. The smaller the angle of bend, the larger the space needed to complete the elevation change (Fig. 30).

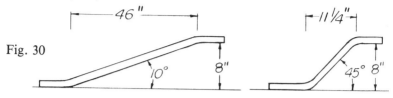

Fig. 30

If space is no problem, the angle of bend should be kept small to make wire pulling easier.

Unlike the 90° stub that is measured over-all, the offset is measured bottom to bottom as shown in Fig. 31.

OFFSET HEIGHT

Once the angle of bend has been decided and the required height of the offset determined, only the spacing between the bends is needed to start bending. This spacing is found by using Trigonometric Functions. Assume an 8″ offset is needed and 30° bends are to be used (Fig. 32).

Fig. 32

The figure forms a right triangle, with the Hypotenuse being the unknown value. As we know the Opposite side (8″) and can find the sine of 30,° we can use the Sine $= \dfrac{O}{H}$ formula.

Sine $= \dfrac{O}{H}$

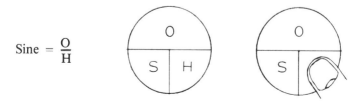

18

Using the magic circle and covering up the unknown value, we can find the Hypotenuse by dividing the Opposite side (8'') by the sine of 30°. Referring to the Trig. Chart, the sine of 30° is .500.

$$H = \frac{O}{S} \qquad H = \frac{8}{.5} \qquad H = 16''$$

Now by placing two marks on the conduit 16'' apart and bending 30° bends, a perfect 8'' offset is achieved as shown in Fig. 33.

Fig. 33

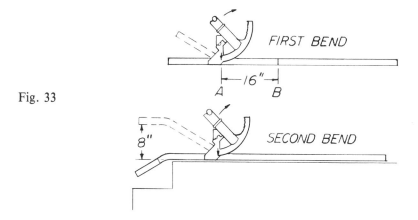

The arrow, front hook of the bender, or any point on the bender can be placed on the marks for bending, but the same spot or point must be used for both the first and the second bend. It is assumed, however, that most hand benders have an arrow or star and all diagrams and descriptions will use the arrow as a reference.

Bend at the first mark. Then roll conduit 180°, taking time to line up the second bend to avoid "dog-legging" the pipe.

NOTE: Marks placed on conduit for bending offsets should be drawn completely around the conduit. This will keep the mark from going out of sight when the pipe is rolled 180° for the second bend.

Use an elevated platform or stairway if available to make the second bend as shown in Fig. 33.

If an elevated platform or stairway is not available, invert the bender and place the handle on the floor to complete the bend. Fig. 34.

Pull down with your hands as close to the bender head as possible to make sure pipe is properly formed in bender shoe.

19

Fig. 34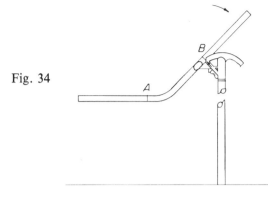

pull down with the hands as close to the bender head as possible and complete second bend.

Care must be taken when the bends are made if perfect results are to be expected. A few degrees too much will make the offset too high and bending less than the required number of degree will make the offset too low.

As we have seen, the spacing between marks can be found using Trigonometric functions, this is time consuming though and is not necessary. A quicker, and more practical method uses the cosecant of the offset angle. The cosecant is the ratio of the hypotenuse to the opposite side (cosecant by degree is listed in the Trigonometric chart).

EXAMPLE: A 10° angle has a cosecant of 5.7587. This tells us that the hypotenuse is 5.7587 times the length of the opposite side. Giving us a multiplier of 5.8 (rounded off).

A 30° angle has a cosecant of 2.0000, or the hypotenuse is 2.0 times as long as the opposite side is tall, giving a multiplier of 2.

To use the cosecant then, all that is required is to know the height (opposite side) of the offset needed. Determine at what angle the offset is to be bent and simply multiply the cosecant of the offset angle times the height to find the spacing between bends (hypotenuse).

To save time, table 35 lists common angles used in offsets and their multipliers. These values should be committed to memory.

Table 35

OFFSET ANGLE	OFFSET MULTIPLIER
10°	5.76
22½°	2.62
30°	2.00
45°	1.41

20

NOTE: Offsets under 15", use only first digit after the decimal.

EXAMPLE: Layout a 12" offset using 45° bends.

The multiplier (cosecant) for 45° bends is 1.4. 1.4 X 12 = 16.8 or approximately 16¾"* between bend mark A and B (Fig. 36).

Fig. 36

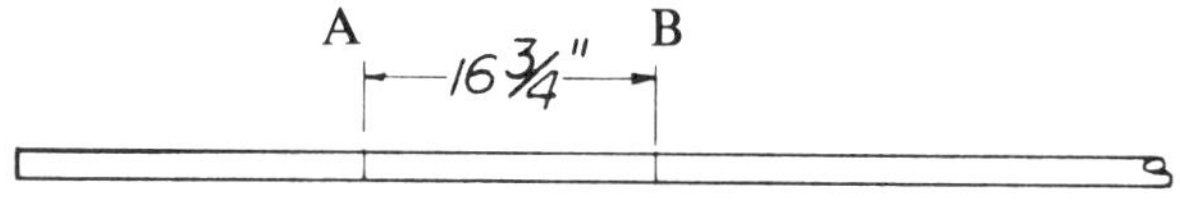

NOTE: This procedure will work for any size conduit, using any style of bender.

TIP: To keep your mental skills alert while bending conduit, try figuring 45° offsets in your head. Let's say you need an 8" offset. Multiply 8" X 1½ (rather than 1.4) to get 12.0". Change the original 8" to .8" and subtract from 12.0".

Answer 11.2" On paper 8" X 1.4 = 11.2"

A 12" offset bending 45°: 12" X 1½ = 18.0, change the original 12" to 1.2" and subtract from 18.0".

Answer 16.8" On paper 12" X 1.4 = 16.8"

45° offsets are the most common offsets used when bending EMT. The fact that a vertical position on the bender handle of many benders indicates 45° makes it a quick process and eliminates the need of using a level. A bender with built in level bubbles to indicate 45 and 90 degree bends is also very popular.

By having a level with a 30° bubble, figuring offsets is simplified as the offset multiplier for 30° offsets is 2. By having 2 as a multiplier, the spacing between the marks can be figured in your head.

The quality built, precision pocket level with both a 45° and 30° bubble is available from:

Four Way Level Co., Inc.
7685 Hwy. 105
Beaumont, TX 77706

The level is magnetized and fully guaranteed.

For bending other angles, a pocket protractor level with magnetic base as shown in Fig. 37 or a magnetic base angle finder (Fig. 38) will be required.

---

*All dimensions are taken to the closest 1/8". As conduit is usually marked with a wide pencil or felt tip pen and the marks are almost an 1/8" wide, there is no sense trying to measure within a 1/16th or 32nd.

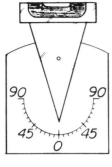

Fig. 37   Fig. 38

Box offsets are the most used offset application. It is not practicable, however, to mark and layout normal box offsets in smaller sized EMT. These offsets are achieved only by practice and for this reason will not be covered. For accurate box offsets in larger conduit sizes, normal offset procedures are necessary.

PROBLEMS: 1. Determine spacing between bend marks for a 22" offset using (a) 45° bends (b) 30° bends (c) 15° bends.

TIP: For offsets in larger sized EMT (above 1¼") when no bender is available. Factory sweeps (elbows) can be cut in half, rotated and coupled together to form an offset. Greater offset depth can be obtained by adding a nipple of the required length.

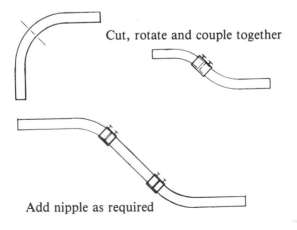

Cut, rotate and couple together

Add nipple as required

22

PRE-DETERMINING OFFSET LOCATION 7

Bending offsets is an easy enough task, once the electrician has learned and developed the proper techniques. Properly aligning the pipe in the bender to avoid "dog-legs" will come quickly with experience.

One of the next steps then, is to learn how to locate the marks on the pipe so the offset location can be pre-determined.

This also is an easy procedure requiring little additional time, but will pay large dividends, in material and labor units saved.

Two methods for pre-determining offset location will be discussed. Study and try both methods, then use the one that you find easiest to apply.

Method #1

The key to this method is establishing "CONSTANTS" for the different pipe sizes, and angle of bends.

This method can be used for any angle offsets and any pipe size.

Notice in Fig. 39 that the right triangle having two 45° bends, the Opposite side and the Adjacent side are of equal length or have a ratio of 1:1. If pipe could be bent like the drawing, to locate the center of bend A, we need only subtract 6" (the length of Adjacent side) from 24" (distance from box to obstruction) to get 18", the location of bend A from the end of the conduit.

Fig. 39

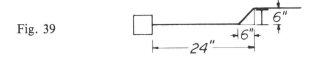

Of course in reality conduit is bent to the radius of the bender shoe as shown in Fig. 40, not at sharp angles as shown in Fig. 39.

Fig. 40

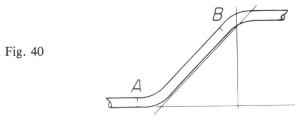

Notice that for a short distance before the right triangle formed at bend A and after bend B, the conduit is not straight. This is caused by the radius of the bend. For the offset to fit properly over the obstruction, the offset must then be located just ahead of the obstruction so the pipe is straight and running true at the obstruction.

To locate the bend marks so that when the offset is completed there is straight pipe at the edge of the obstruction, an amount is added to the Adjacent side measurement before subtracting from the distance from the box to the obstruction. The amount that must be added for 45° offsets can be found as follows:

1. Bend a 45° bend in a scrap piece of pipe.
2. Locate and mark the center of the bend.
3. Using the bender handle as a straight edge, measure from the center of the bend to a point where the conduit is straight on the bender handle (Fig. 41).

Fig. 41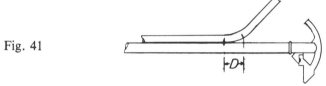

This amount (D) X 2 is the amount that must be added to the Adjacent side dimension before subtracting from the dimension from the box to obstruction to compensate for bending on a radius.

The amount that is added is called an **Offset Constant** and will be different for each pipe size and angle of offset.

For 45° bends only, the following amounts (to be called constants) have been established for the following EMT pipe sizes to compensate for the radius of both bends of the offset.

EMT Size	Add
½"	5"
¾"	6¼"
1"	7½"

For 45° offsets the height of the obstruction (Opposite side) is equal to the Adjacent side or has a ratio of 1:1. With this fact in mind we can add the constant for ½" EMT (5") to the height of the obstruction and subtract from the distance between box and obstruction to locate bend mark A.

NOTE: For simplicity, examples and problems will be drawn in one line form, and box offsets will not be included.

EXAMPLE: A 6" "I" beam is located 28" from a box. Using 45° bends and ½" EMT, layout bend marks A & B.

24

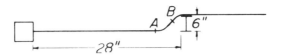

Height of obstruction	6"
Constant ½" EMT	+ 5"
Total	11"

Distance from box to obstruction	28"
	-11"
Equals	17"

Measuring from end of conduit, place bend mark A at 17". Multiply 1.4 (cosecant of 45°) X 6" (height of "I" beam) to find spacing between bend marks A and B. 1.4 X 6" = 8.4" or approximately 8 3/8"

NOTE: See decimal to fraction conversion chart in back of book.

EXAMPLE: ¾" EMT must be bent as indicated. Locate bend marks A and B.

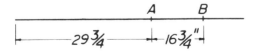

1. Height of obstruction (12") added to constant for ¾" EMT (6¼") equals 18¼".

2. Distance from box to "I" beam (48") minus 18¼" equals 29¾".

3. From the end of the pipe measure 29¾" and mark bend mark A.

4. Multiply height of obstruction (12") times 1.4 to find spacing between bend marks A and B. 12" X 1.4 = 16.8" or approximately 16¾".

5. Mark conduit and bend.

PROBLEMS: Layout pipe to bend as indicated. All offsets 45°, EMT size as indicated.

25

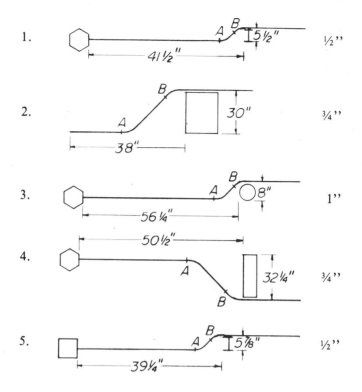

1.   ½"

2.   ¾"

3.   1"

4.   ¾"

5.   ½"

To pre-position offsets for other than 45° bends, we will use offset **location** multipliers. These multipliers will be used **only** for locating the first bend mark of the offset and MUST NOT be confused with offset multiplers that are used to find the spacing between the bend marks (A and B).

For 45° offsets we found that the height of the obstruction (Opposite side) was equal to the Adjacent side or the ratio of opposite to Adjacent was 1:1. For any other angle of offset bends the ratio will be different.

EXAMPLE: Offsets bent using 30° bends will have a ratio of 1:1.73 between the Opposite (height of obstruction) and the Adjacent side (Fig. 42).

Fig. 42

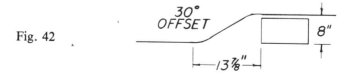

26

We can prove the ratio by using the formula $T = \dfrac{O}{A}$

By dividing the Opposite side (8") by the Tangent of 30° (.5774) we can determine the Adjacent side.

$$\text{Adjacent side} = \frac{O}{T}$$

$$\text{Adjacent side} = \frac{8}{.5774}$$

Adjacent side = 13.86 or approximately 13 7/8"

To find the ratio of the Opposite to the Adjacent side we divide the Adjacent side (13.86) by the Opposite side (8").

$$\text{Ratio} = \frac{\text{Adjacent side}}{\text{Opposite Side}}$$

$$\text{Ratio} = \frac{13.86}{8} = 1.73$$

$$\text{Ratio} = 1{:}1.73$$

This tells us that for an offset bent with 30° bends the Adjacent side will always be 1.73 times longer than the height of the obstruction or Opposite side. The ratio of 1:1.73 will be true no matter what size pipe is used and no matter what the height of the obstruction may be. If the ratio is always true, the height of the obstruction can be multiplied by 1.73 to find the length of the Adjacent side for pre-positioning offsets using Method #1. Stated another way, the 1.73 becomes a **Location** multiplier.

The constant used to compensate for bending on a radius and to assure straight pipe where the pipe crosses over the obstruction also changes as the angle of offset bends change. Table 43 lists the constants for 45°, 30°, 22½° and 10° offsets when using ½", ¾" and 1" EMT.

Table 43

ANGLE OF OFFSET	EMT PIPE SIZE		
	1/2"	3/4"	1"
45°	5"	6¼"	7¼"
30°	4½"	5½"	6"
22½°	3½"	4¼"	4 3/4"
10°	3"	3½"	4"

NOTE: For other offset angles use the procedure discussed earlier and as shown in Fig. 41.

PROBLEM: Locate the bend marks to pre-position a 10" offset with ½" EMT using 30° bends.

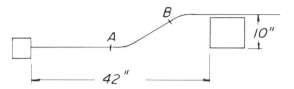

1. Multiply the height of the obstruction (10") times the location multiplier for 30° offsets (1.73).
10 X 1.73 = 17.3 or approximately 17¼".

2. Add the constant for 30° bends to compensate for bending on a radius (4½") as found in Table 43, to the Adjacent side (17¼") to find the amount that is subtracted from the box (or end of pipe) to the obstruction (42") to locate bend mark A.
4½" + 17¼" = 21¾"
42" minus 21¾" = 20¼" from end of pipe to bend mark A.

3. The distance between bend mark A and B is found by multiplying the height of the obstruction (10") times the offset multiplier (2.0).
10" X 2 = 20"

For pre-position offsets using Method #1, Table 44 gives the location multiplier for offsets using 45°, 30°, 22½° and 10° bends. The location multiplier for other offset angles is the Cotangent of the angle and can be found in the Trig Chart at the back of the book.

Table 44

OFFSET ANGLE	LOCATION MULTIPLIER
45°	1.00
30°	1.73
22½°	2.42
10°	5.67

PROBLEM: Locate the bend marks for a 6" offset using 22½ ° bends and ¾" EMT.

1. Height X location multiplier for 22½ ° offsets (2.42) as found in Table 44 or by looking up the Cotangent of 22½ °.
6 X 2.42 = 14.52 or approximately 14½".
2. Add the constant for 22½ ° offset using ¾" EMT (4¼") as shown in Table 43.
14½" + 4¼" = 18¾"
3. Subtract from the distance from the box to the obstruction (58") to locate bend mark A.

$$\begin{array}{r} 58" \\ - \ 18\frac{3}{4}" \\ \hline 39\frac{1}{4}" \end{array}$$

4. Multiply the height of the obstruction (6") times the offset multiplier for 22½ ° offsets (2.6) to find the spacing between bend marks A and B.
6 X 2.6 = 15.6 or approximately 15 5/8"

Method #2

This method requires the use of "SHRINK" values.

Shrink is the amount the over-all length of a pipe will shorten (or shrink) when the offset is bent.

To determine shrink for a given offset angle, proceed as follows:
1. Measure overall length of a scrap piece of pipe (36") as shown in Fig. 45a.

Fig. 45a

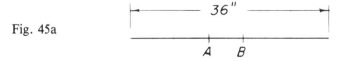

2. Calculate spacing between the bend marks for an offset height of 8" using 30° bends (16").

3. Bend the offset and measure the distance from one end of the conduit to the other end as shown in Fig. 45b.

Fig. 45b

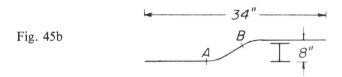

4. Subtract the new length (34") from the original overall length (36") to find total shrink (2").

5. Divide total shrink (2") by the height of the offset (8") to find shrink per inch of offset rise.

$$\frac{2''}{8''} = .25 \text{ or } \frac{1}{4}''$$

This amount, ¼" of shrink per inch of offset height (or rise), can be used to find the amount of shrink for any height of offset that is bent with 30° bends.

EXAMPLE: Find the total shrink for a 14" offset using 30° bends.

$$14'' \times \frac{1}{4}'' = \frac{14}{4} \text{ or } 3\frac{1}{2}'' \text{ Total Shrink.}$$

Once the shrink value has been found for a given offset angle, the value will apply to any size conduit (EMT or Rigid).

Table 46 shows the shrink values for the most common offset angles.

Table 46

ANGLE	SHRINK PER INCH OF OFFSET RISE
10°	1/16"
22½°	3/16"
30°	1/4"
45°	3/8"
60°	1/2"

NOTE: To find the shrink values for other angles of bend, locate the cotangent for the offset angle in the Trig. Chart and subtract this value from the cosecant of the same angle. Convert decimal to fractions of an inch, for shrink per inch of rise. These will be purely mathematical values and will be very close, for more accurate values bend a scrap piece of pipe to determine shrink per inch of rise.

Fig. 47 shows an offset consisting of two 30° bends, and a 10" rise. By using the shrink value for 30° (¼"), you need only multiply this value times the offset height (10") to get total shrink.

Fig. 47

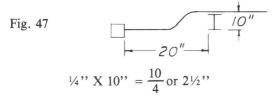

$$\text{¼}" \times 10" = \frac{10}{4} \text{ or } 2\text{½}"$$

If the pipe is 60" long it will shorten or "shrink" 2½" to 57½" overall after the two 30° bends are made. Likewise, a mark placed on the conduit will end up 2½" closer to the box once the pipe has been bent.

By knowing how much the mark will move allows us to mark the conduit and pre-position the offset.

By measuring the distance from the box (Fig. 47) to the front edge of the obstruction (20") and adding to this measurement the shrink value for a 10" offset using 30° bends (2½"), we can place a mark on the conduit that will end up at the front edge of the obstruction after the offset is bent (Figs. 48a and 48b).

Fig. 48a

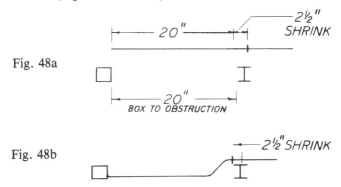

Fig. 48b

After the offset is bent, the pipe shrink will move the mark 2½" toward the box and the mark ends up at the edge of the obstruction.

By using this mark (distance + shrink) as bend mark B we can pre-position the bend marks so the finished offset will fit perfectly from the box to the obstruction.

The actual bending will require that we turn our back on the end of the conduit that we measured from. This will put the bend itself to the left of the bend mark B and leave straight pipe to cross over the obstruction as shown in Fig. 49. Bend at bend mark B first and then bend mark A.

31

Fig. 49

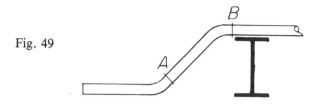

EXAMPLE: A 6" "I" beam is located 28" from a box. Using 30°
bends, layout bend mark A and B.

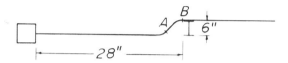

Total shrink value is found by multiplying height of offset (6") times
the 30° shrink value (¼" per inch of offset rise). Total shrink equals
6" X ¼" or 1½".

Add total shrink (1½") to distance from box to obstruction (28") to
locate bend mark B.

$$\begin{array}{r} 28" \\ +\ 1½" \\ \hline 29½"\ \text{Total} \end{array}$$

Measure 29½" from end of conduit and mark bend mark B. Spacing
between A and B is found by multiplying 30° multiplier (2) times
height of offset (6").

2 X 6" = 12" Spacing

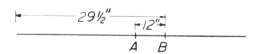

EXAMPLE: A conduit is to be bent as indicated. Using 45° offsets,
layout bend marks A and B.

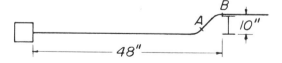

1. Determine total shrink by multiplying the height of offset times 45°
shrink value (3/8" per inch rise).

32

Height of offset 10"

$$\begin{array}{r} X \quad 3/8" \\ \hline \text{Total} \quad 3\frac{3}{4}" \end{array}$$

2. Add total shrink to distance from box to obstruction.

Total Shrink	3¾"
Distance	+48"
Total	51¼"

3. Measure 51¼" from end of conduit and mark bend mark B.

4. Multiply height of offset (10") times 45° offset multiplier (1.4) to determine spacing between bend mark A and B (14")

5. Mark conduit with bend mark A. Remember to turn your back on the end of the conduit that measurements were taken from and also to bend at bend mark B first.

PROBLEMS: Layout pipe to bend as indicated.

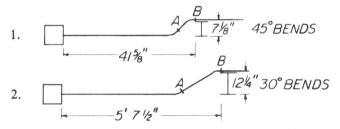

PARALLEL OFFSETS   8

For bending parallel offsets as shown in Fig. 50a, an adjustment must be made to the layout of the second and each subsequent pipe in the group to prevent the ends from being staggered.

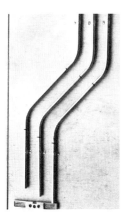

Fig. 50a

Fig. 50b shows three other ½" pieces of EMT with 10" offsets but with the bend marks adjusted so the pipes are even when positioned and 2" spacing is maintained.

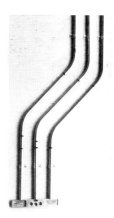

Fig. 50b

NOTE: A 12" reference mark was placed on pipe "A", "B" and "C" in Fig. 50b for illustration only, and is not necessary for actual bending layout.

The amount of adjustment to the start mark may be found by using the following formula.

Adjustment = Center to center spacing X tangent of ½ the offset angle.

EXAMPLE: The 10" offsets shown in Fig. 50b are bent with 45° angles. One half (½) of 45° is 22½°. The tangent for 22½° is approximately .4142. The center to center spacing between conduit A & B is 2.706 (Fig. 51).

34

Fig. 51

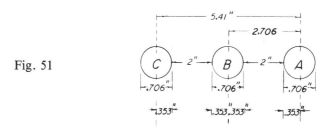

The spacing (2.706) times the tangent for 22½° (.4142) gives us 1.12" or approximately 1 1/8". Pipe A in Fig. 50b had a start mark of 12" so the value 1 1/8" is the amount that must be added to the start mark of pipe B for the pipes to come out even at the ends when 2" spacing is maintained. 12" + 1 1/8" = 13 1/8" start mark for pipe B (Fig. 52).

Fig. 52

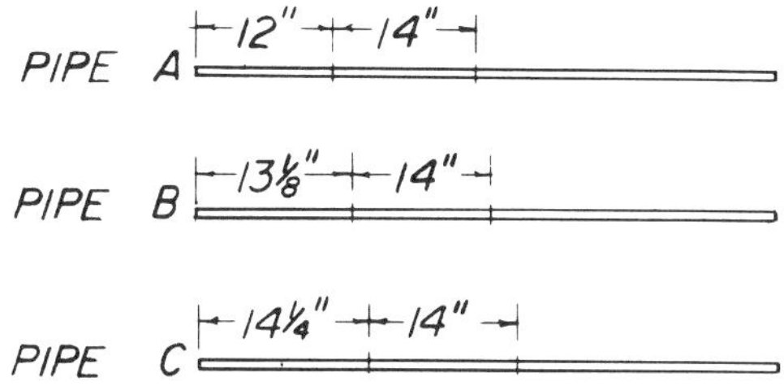

PIPE A

PIPE B

PIPE C

To find the adjustment to the start mark for pipe C, we use the same formula as before, but the spacing used will be from pipe A (the first pipe bent) to pipe C. Referring again to Fig. 51, we see the center to center spacing between pipes A & C is 5.41". This distance (5.41") times the tangent for 22½° (.4142) equals 2.24" or approximately 2¼". This value (2¼") is added to the start mark of pipe A (12") to give us a 14¼" start mark for pipe C (Fig. 52).

The center to center spacing between pipe B & C could also be used, .353" + 2" + .353" = 2.706" and the calculated adjustment (2.706" X .4142) 1 1/8" added to the 13 1/8" start mark of pipe B, to give us (13 1/8" + 1 1/8") 14¼" start mark for pipe C.

NOTE: This procedure will only work when the same size conduit is bent using the same bender **or** when different size pipes are bent using the same bender or bending shoe.

Using the same bender for EMT will work with ½" and ¾" pipe bent with a ¾" shoe (Fig. 53), but the author has had little success trying to bend ½", ¾" and 1" EMT with a 1" bender or even ¾" and 1" on a 1" shoe.

35

Fig. 53

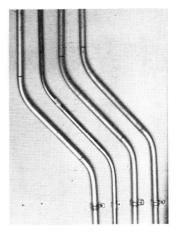

Rigid pipe sizes ½", ¾" and 1", however, can be successfully bent on the 1" shoe of a "CHICAGO" type bender (Fig. 54).

Fig. 54

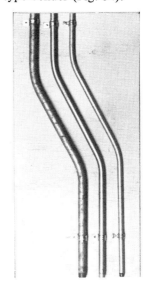

1¼", 1½" and 2" pipe may all be bent on a hydraulic bender using the 2" shoe and pivot supports. When bending one-shot bends with hydraulic benders, the start mark will be the center of the first bend of the offset on each pipe and will be adjusted for the second and each additional pipe in the rack using the formula as outlined.

The spacing between the first and second bend marks on the pipe for the offset itself remain constant for all conduits in the group (Fig. 52).

The rigid pipe spacing chart at the back of the book will be helpful for layout when using this procedure.

FOUR BEND SADDLES 9

A saddle is a series of bends to change elevation to clear an obstruction and then return to the original elevation (Fig. 55), or simply double offsets.

Fig. 55

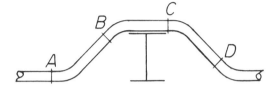

Fig. 55

As with offset bending, extreme care must be taken to properly align the pipe in the bender. Carelessness will produce a saddle that is badly "dog-legged" which will require major adjustments to be useable, or may be so bad it cannot be corrected and will end up in the "oh-oh" pile.

To bend the saddle as shown in Fig. 55.

1. Measure height and width of the obstruction.

2. Determine spacing between marks A and B for first offset (height of obstruction X offset multiplier). This will also be the spacing between the second offset marks C and D.

3. Bend first offset (bends A and B).

4. Starting from where pipe is straight after the second bend of the first offset, measure over the width of the obstruction and mark pipe. This is mark C, the first bend mark of the second offset. Measure over required spacing (height of obstruction X offset multiplier) and mark D, second bend, second offset.

5. Bend second offset (bends C and D).

Saddle is complete (Fig. 56).

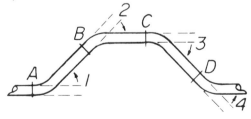

Fig. 56

Complete bends in sequence indicated Steps 1 through 4.

To Pre-determine Saddle Location

Installation location (reached from a ladder, scaffolding, swinging platform, etc.) will probably dictate whether the extra time spent pre-determining saddle locations is beneficial. For rigid conduit, where cutting plus threading is required, there is no doubt the additional time spent will save money.

This procedure is simplified by marking the conduit with a reference ("R") point.

The reference ("R") point will indicate location of the edge of the obstruction after the first offset is bent. The reference point then, is the distance to the obstruction plus shrink (Fig. 57). The width of the obstruction is then measured over from "R" to locate the first bend mark of the **second** offset.

Fig. 57

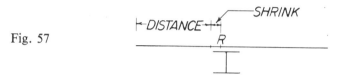

R = Distance plus shrink of one offset.*

R will move to the left and be at the edge of the obstruction after the first offset is bent. This fact makes R a valid reference point for laying out the second offset.

Pre-determining offset location using Method #1 and #2 (preceding Chapter) may now be applied to locate the **first** offset bend marks.

METHOD #1

EXAMPLE: A beam 8" high and 10" wide located 32" from the box is to be saddled using ½" EMT and 45° bends.

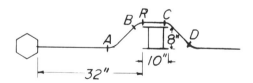

---

*The pipe will have shrunk when each offset is bent, so the total shrink of the pipe would be 2 times height of one offset X shrink value for the angle of offset bends.

To locate bend marks:

1. Locate bend mark A.
Height (8") plus 45° constant (5") subtracted from distance (32")
8" + 5" = 13"
Distance to A = 32" - 13" = 19"
Measure 19" from end of conduit and mark bend mark A.
2. Determine spacing between A and B (also spacing between C and D)
Height (8") X 45° multiplier (1.4).
8" X 1.4 = 11.2 or approximately 11¼"
Measure from A over 11¼" and mark bend mark B.
3. Locate R.
R = Distance + Shrink for one offset.
Find shrink for one offset.
Shrink = Height (8") X shrink value 45° (3/8").
8" X 3/8 = 24/8 or 3"
Distance (32") + shrink (3") = 35"
4. Measure 35" from end of conduit and mark R.
5. Bend mark C must be located the width of obstruction (10") from the reference mark R. Measure over 10" from R and mark bend mark C.
6. Measure spacing from C to D 11¼" (Same as spacing from A to B).

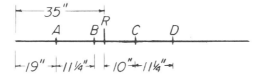

The conduit bending sequence will be bend A, bend B, bend C and bend D. All bends made facing the end of the pipe measurements were taken from (Fig. 58).

NOTE: R is for reference **ONLY,** not a bend mark.

Fig. 58

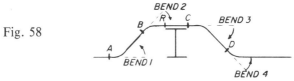

METHOD #2

1. Find shrink.
Shrink = Height (8") X shrink value 45° (3/8").
8" X 3/8" = 24/8 or 3"

2. Locate mark B.
Distance (32") plus shrink (3").
32" + 3"
Bend Mark B = 35"
Measure 35" from end of conduit and mark B.

3. Determine spacing between A and B (also spacing between C and D).
Height (8") X 45° multiplier (1.4).
8" X 1.4 = 11.2 or approximately 11¼"
Measure from B to A = 11¼".

4. Locate bend C.
Bend B plus width of obstruction (10"). Measure over 10" from B and mark, C.

5. Measure spacing from C to D 11¼" (same as spacing from A to B).

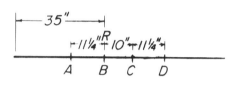

The bending sequence using this method is important if all bends are to be made properly. With your back to the end you measured from, bend at bend mark B first, and then at bend mark A. Now facing the end you measured from, bend pipe at bend mark C and then bend at mark D (Fig. 59).

Fig. 59

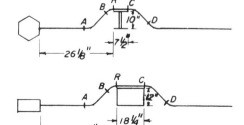

NOTE: Bend Mark B and R are the same.

PROBLEMS:
Method #1

1. ½" EMT 45° Bends

2. ¾" EMT 45° Bends

40

Method #2

1. 1" EMT 30° Bends

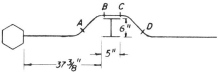

2. ½" EMT 45° Bends

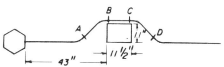

THREE BEND SADDLES 10

As the name implies, this saddle requires three bends rather than four as a normal saddle (Fig. 60). This saddle is used primarily to go over pipe or round obstructions.

Fig. 60

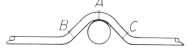

The three bend saddle requires one 45° bend (A) and two, 22½° bends (B and C).

Notice that bend mark A (the 45° bend) must end up in the center of the bend.

Most benders have a spot marked on the bending shoe that is used to indicate center of bend. If your bender has no such mark: bend a piece of scrap pipe at 45°, mark center of bend and place corresponding mark on bender as shown in Fig. 61. This mark then is used for bending the 45° bend (bend mark A) instead of the arrow.

Mark pipe at center of 45° bend

Fig. 61

Mark bender shoe to establish center of bend mark.

41

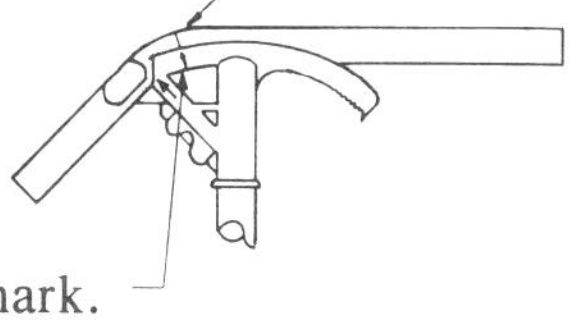

Bend marks B and C (the 22½ ° bends) are located equal distance from bend mark A and will use the arrow on the bender.

To determine the spacing from A to B and A to C we simply multiply the height of the obstruction times 2.5. The multiplier of 2.5 is used for all pipe sizes.

EXAMPLE: Layout a three bend saddle to clear an 8'' pipe.

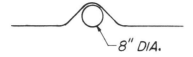

8" DIA.

1. Determine spacing from bend mark A to B and A to C.
Spacing = 2.5 X Height (8'').
2.5 X 8'' = 20''
Spacing = 20''
2. Bend mark A is placed at approximate center of conduit.
3. Locate marks B and C, 20'' either side of bend mark A.

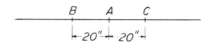

4. Bend as indicated in Fig. 62. Bend a 45 ° bend at bend mark A. Be sure and use the mark on the bender that indicates center of bend, **NOT** the arrow.

Fig. 62

The bender is removed and turned so both bends B and C are made facing bend A. Remember that bend A uses the mark on the bender that indicates center of bend and that bends B and C use the arrow.

5. Cut end of pipe as required to fit.

TIP: For the two 22½ ° bends, invert the bender placing the handle vertical with the floor. If the pipe was bent to 45 °, it would be horizontal to the work surface, so bending half way will produce a 22½ ° bend. Only a few trial bends are required before you can produce good results using this method.

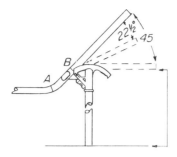

If it is more desirable to bend all three bends facing the same direction, it can be done by using a multiplier of 3 and by bending all bends (A, B and C) using the mark on the bender that represents the center of the bend.

NOTE: This method can be used for hand benders and is the recommended method for **"CHICAGO"** type benders.

EXAMPLE: Layout a three bend saddle to clear 8" pipe.

1. Determine spacing from bend mark A to B and A to C.
Spacing = 3 X Height (8")
3 X 8" = 24"
Spacing = 24"
2. Bend mark A is placed at approximate center of conduit.
3. Locate marks B and C 24" either side of bend mark A.
4. Bend all bends using the center of bend indicating mark NOT THE ARROW and all bends are made facing the same end of the pipe (Fig. 63).

Fig. 63

Pre-Determined Saddle Location

To save cutting pipe, the center of the saddle (center of obstruction) can be pre-determined by adding shrink to the distance required. The saddle requires one 45° bend and two 22½° bends, as the two 22½° bends total 45° the 45° offset shrink (3/8") can be used to find total shrink of the pipe. We are concerned with locating the center of the obstruction from only one end of the conduit, so only ½ the total shrink is used (Fig. 64). This method of predetermining saddle location is used whether a multiplier of 2.5 or 3 is used.

43

Fig. 64

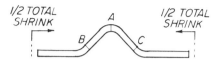

EXAMPLE: Layout bend marks for three bend saddle to clear a 6" pipe located 30" from a box to center of pipe.

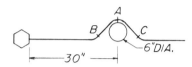

1. Find total shrink for pipe.
Height of saddle (6") X shrink value 45° (3/8")
6" X 3/8" = 18/8 or 2¼"
Total Shrink = 2¼"
2. Locate bend mark A.
Distance from box to center of pipe (30") plus ½ total shrink (1 1/8")
30" + 1 1/8" = 31 1/8"
Distance from end of pipe to A = 31 1/8"
3. Measure 31 1/8" from end of conduit and mark A.
4. Determine spacing from A to B and A to C. Spacing = 2.5 or 3 X Height of obstruction (6") depending on bending technique used:
Spacing = 2.5 X Height of obstruction
2.5 X 6 = 15" Spacing
5. Locate mark B and C 15" either side of mark A.
6. Bend 45° at mark A (mark to be center of bend) Bend 22½° bends at B and C (use arrow and bend as indicated in Fig. 62).

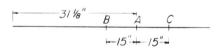

7. To find spacing using a multiplier of 3:
Spacing = 3 X Height of obstruction
3 X 6 + 18" Spacing
8. Locate marks B and C 18" either side of mark A (Fig. 65).
9. Using the mark that indicates center of the bend NOT THE ARROW, bend 22½° at bend mark B, bend 45° at bend mark A and bend a 22½° bend at C. All bends are made facing the end of the conduit you measured from.

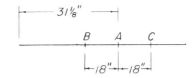

Fig. 65

PROBLEMS:

Using a multiplier of 2.5

1.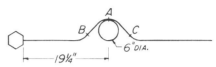

2.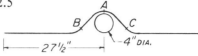

Using a multiplier of 3

3.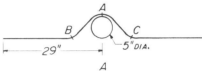

4.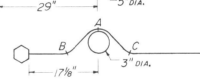

BENDING AROUND A CORNER WITH AN OBSTRUCTION   11

Although this is not a common bending job, it is one that can become very frustrating if the proper method is not known.

The following examples (Fig. 66a, b and c) are the most common types of obstructions that are encountered. The pipe is bent with two 45° bends. For each type of obstruction a formula is given to determine the spacing between bend marks.

Fig. 66a

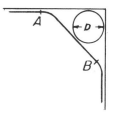

Round Obstruction
D X 2.4 = spacing between bend marks

Fig. 66b

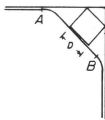

Square Obstruction
D X 3 = spacing between the bend marks

Fig. 66c

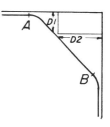

Rectangular Obstruction
$D^1 + D^2$ X 1.4 = spacing between bend marks

The arrow or front of the shoe is placed on the bend marks as indicated below in Fig. 67.

Fig. 67

A 45° bend is made at bend mark A and a 45° bend is made at bend mark B. Both bends must be made facing the same direction.

EXAMPLE: Formula: D X 2.4 = spacing between bend marks.

D (6'') X 2.4 = 14.4 or approximately 14 3/8''

Formula: $D^1 + D^2 \times 1.4$ = spacing between bend marks.

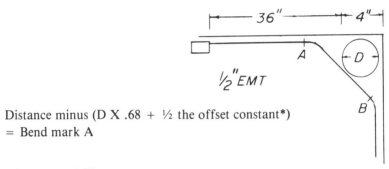

D^1 (6") + D^2 (8") $\times$ 1.4 = 19.74 or approximately 19¾"

NOTE: These same formulas and layout may be used with "CHICAGO" type benders.

For preposition bend marks the following formulas are used.

ROUND OBSTRUCTIONS:

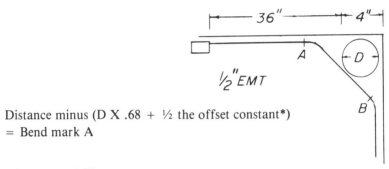

Distance minus (D $\times$ .68 + ½ the offset constant*)
= Bend mark A

Distance = 36"
Diameter = 4"
Diameter 4" $\times$ .68 = 2.72 or approximately 2¾".
½ offset constant for ½" EMT (5") = 2½"
36" minus (2¾" + 2½") = Bend mark A
36" minus 5¼" = 30¾" from end of pipe to bend mark A.
Spacing from A to B is found by multiplying diameter (D) $\times$ 2.4.
4" $\times$ 2.4 = 9.6 or approximately 9 5/8"

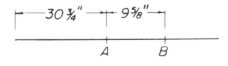

---

*Constant for bending on a radius used for pre-positioning offsets Method #1.

47

SQUARE OBSTRUCTION:

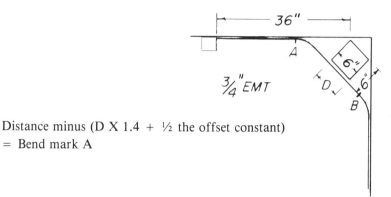

Distance minus (D X 1.4 + ½ the offset constant)
= Bend mark A

Distance = 36"
D = 6"
D X 1.4 = 8.4" or approximately 8 3/8"
½ offset constant for ¾" EMT (6¼") = 3 1/8"
36" minus (8 3/8" + 3 1/8") = Bend mark A
36" minus 11½" = 24½" from end of pipe to bend mark A.
Spacing from A to B is found by using the formula.
Spacing = D X 3
Spacing = 6" X 3
Spacing = 18"

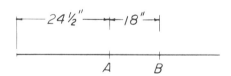

RECTANGULAR OBSTRUCTIONS:

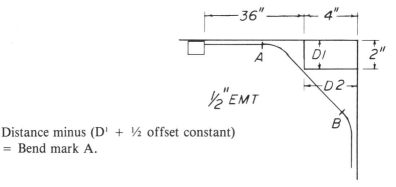

Distance minus (D^1 + ½ offset constant)
= Bend mark A.

Distance = 36"
D^1 = 2"
½ offset constant for ½" EMT (5") = 2½"
36" minus (2" + 2½") = Bend mark A.
36" minus 4½" = 31½" from end of pipe to bend mark A.
Spacing from bend mark A to bend mark B is found by using the following formula;
Spacing = D^1 + D^2 X 1.4
Spacing = 2" + 4" X 1.4
Spacing = 6" X 1.4
Spacing = 8.4 or approximately 8 3/8"

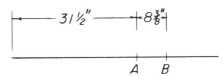

RIGID METAL CONDUIT   12

Rigid Metal Conduit includes pipe made of Ferrous (Steel) and Nonferrous (Aluminum, Copper, Bronze, etc.) materials.

National Electrical Code® rules governing its use and installation are covered by NEC Article 346.

Standard Rigid trade sizes are: ½", ¾", 1", 1¼", 1½", 2", 2½", 3", 3½", 4", 4½", 5" and 6".

Rigid conduit is manufactured in standard 10' lengths (measurement includes the coupling which is furnished with each piece of pipe). Each end is threaded with standard ¾" per foot tapered thread.

Bending qualities will be effected by the ductility, uniformity and surface treatment of the conduit and these qualities will vary with the manufacturer.

The minimum bend radius for field bends (any bend made by the electrician for installation of the conduit) are covered in NEC Article 346 Tables 346-10 and 346-10 Exception.

The CODE also limits the number of bends between boxes, outlets, etc. to four quarter bends (360° total), this includes box offsets.

RIGID PIPE BENDERS: Rigid Pipe may be bent using a Hickey, "CHICAGO" type bender, Full Shoe Electric or Hydraulic bender.

Hand bending with a hickey (Fig. 68) is not for precision bending and its use is usually restricted to imbedded and underground installations. Effective bending with the hickey is limited to ½", ¾" and 1" sizes. Conduit above these sizes require too much physical strength for one man to handle.

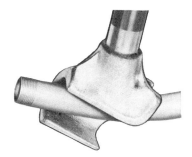

Fig. 68
Courtesy — Greenlee Tool Co.

"CHICAGO" type benders (Fig. 69) will bend rigid steel pipe up to 1½" and EMT and aluminum conduit up to 2" trade size. The bender pictured is the ENERPAC "Side Winder".

Fig. 69
Courtesy — ENERPAC Co.

The electrical bender shown in Fig. 70a will bend not only ½"
through 2" Rigid and Aluminum conduit but will also bend ½"
through 2" EMT and IMC. No need to change shoes, as the shoes are
all included in one casting. Though the shoe design is convenient,
what makes the Enerpac CYCLON ™ bender unique is the solid state
circuitry that allows you to "dial in" the desired angle of bend from
1 ° to 105 ° (Fig. 70b). The CYCLON ™ even compensates for "spring
back" and gives you a perfect bend everytime.

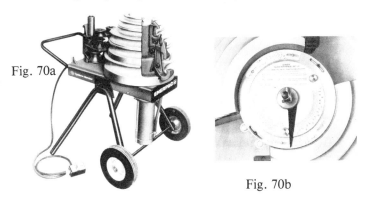

Fig. 70a

Fig. 70b

HYDRAULIC benders (Fig. 71 & 72) will bend all rigid pipe sizes and
are available with segment or one-shot shoes (one-shot bending up to
4" trade size).

Fig. 71 Segment Bender

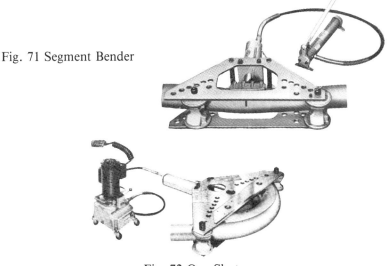

Fig. 72 One-Shot
Courtesy — Greenlee Tool Co.

Bending Rigid Pipe

HICKEY METHOD: As with hand EMT benders, constant pressure must be applied with the foot to prevent irregular bends. As there is no foot piece on a hickey, this pressure must be applied to the pipe just back of the bender (Fig. 73a and b).

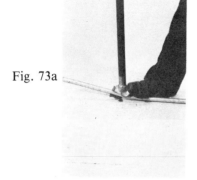

Fig. 73a

Fig. 73b

Although accurate bending with a hickey is difficult without many hours of experience, acceptable bends can be made by the beginner.

Rough take-up* values for figuring stubs are as follows:

Pipe Size	Take-up
½"	5"
¾"	7"
1"	9"

90° hickey bends must not be made with one setting of the bender. Although a 90° stub could be made without collapsing the pipe in only one setting, the radius of bend would be too sharp and make wire pulling difficult, if not impossible. The correct method then is to set the bender, pull a small degree bend, slide the bender down on the pipe (called a "bite") and bend again. Continue moving (sliding) bender and bending until full 90° bend is achieved. This method is called "inching" and makes a larger, smoother radius bend (Fig. 74).

---

*Take-up will vary with hickey type used and material conduit is made of. Use these take-up figures and layout pipe as described for 90° stubs in the EMT section.

Fig. 74

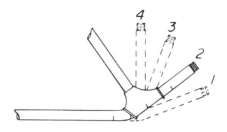

After the third or fourth bend, check the developing stub length. If it is going to come up short, take a deeper "bite" on the pipe with the bender to compensate. If the stub length is coming up long, reverse hickey head on pipe and remove some of the bend, reset hickey and take shorter "bites" with more bend per "bite." If a smooth radius is not necessary, after removing some of the bend, move bender higher on to stub and pull a sharper bend to complete the 90° stub.

For offsets, saddles, kicks, etc. all information as to layout and procedure found in the EMT section will apply. Do not expect precision results, they are not easily obtained with a hickey. If precision bending is required, use a "CHICAGO" bender.

"CHICAGO" TYPE BENDER METHODS 13

The "CHICAGO" type bender (Fig. 75) is the ultimate in benders for smaller size conduit. With care and proper procedure, conduit bending becomes an art form. Not all electricians are capable, nor aspire to this degree of proficiency, but for the electrician who does, this is the tool that makes it possible.

Fig. 75
Photo Courtesy — Enerpac Co.

Bending jobs on this type bender are easier if two electricians can work together, one for alignment and leveling, the other for operating the ratchet handle for bending. Although more time consuming, one person can operate the bender successfully.

To use the "CHICAGO" type bender requires little new information. Some basic terminology of the bender though will be helpful (Fig. 76).

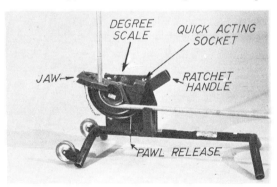

Fig. 76 The original "CHICAGO" bender

The "jaw" or front of the bending shoe will be used for reference, the same way the arrow of the EMT hand bender was used.

Pawl release disengages the ratchet mechanism so bent pipe can be removed or moved forward.

All benders of this type have a degree scale indicator. The accuracy of these scales is questionable, especially on older or well used benders. The scale can still be used if some scrap pieces of pipe are bent and

54

notations or corrective marks (in pencil) are made. The same procedure should be used for determining take-up. Bend some sample bends and mark take-up on the shoe. Don't depend on existing marks or notations made by others. You are responsible for the conduit you bend, so establish your own figures.

For accuracy of bends and ease of bending, level the bender frame. If the work surface is rough and uneven, use a piece of plywood or other wood members as needed. By having the frame level, precision offsets, 90° stubs and multiple bend pipe jobs are greatly simplified and produce results that you can take pride in.

Figuring and layout as described in the EMT section will apply for 90° stubs, kicks, offsets and saddles. These procedures gain added importance when working with rigid conduit that must be cut, reamed and threaded. Pipe that fits the first time without cutting and threading or adding nipples to make it fit, more than pays for the little extra time spent on pre-figuring pipe layout.

As discussed earlier, the success of formulated bending is dependent on precision bent angles. As previously stated, the degree indicator on the bender is of questionable value and many pocket protractor levels also lack the required accuracy. The magnetic angle finder has a high degree of accuracy and is an indispensable tool for the serious conduit bender (Fig. 77). Whether or not this tool is available, an alternate method for bending angles less than 90° is the "amount of travel method." This method requires no tools or device other than your rule and pencil.

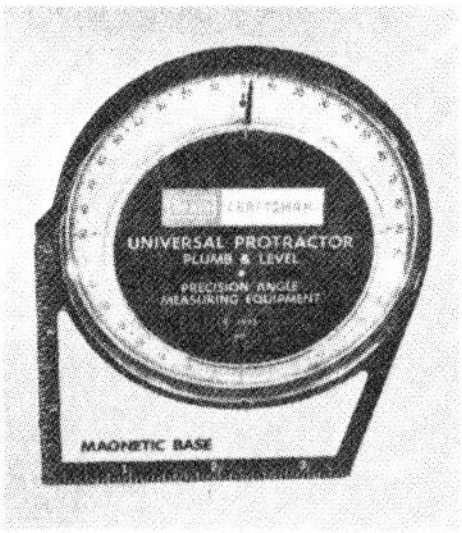

Fig. 77

Amount of Travel Method

The basis for this method is the fact that for a given pipe size, the same amount of pipe will be drawn (travel) into the bender and formed around the radius of the bending shoe every time.

There then must exist a relationship between the amount of conduit travel and degree of bend.

Example: If 10'' of conduit travels into the bender for a 90° bend, only 5'' should travel into the bender for a 45° bend.

To apply the method:

1. Carefully level the bender frame.

55

2. Insert straight length of conduit into bender. Attach front jaw, release pawl, lift handle to engage the ratchet and then lower the handle, letting the weight of the handle hold conduit in place.

3. Using the back conduit support, bending shoe back plate assembly or other convenient non moving bender part as a reference, place a mark on the conduit. Use a level or other straight edge (Fig. 78).

Fig. 78

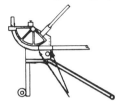

Place marks on conduit using bender shoe backplate as shown

4. Bend a full ninety, checking carefully with a level for accuracy and accounting for "spring-back" (the amount that bent pipe tends to straighten when pressure is released).

5. Using same spot on bender, mark pipe again.

6. Remove pipe from bender and measure distance between marks.

This measurement then is travel in inches for a 90° bend.

To find amount of travel for any given angle less than ninety degrees — divide the angle into ninety and that sum into travel in inches.

EXAMPLE: Total 90° travel is 8¾''. Find travel for (A) 22½° (B) 10°.

HINT: Convert fractions to decimal equivalent. (Conversion chart is found in the back of the book) Then convert final answer back to closest fraction.

(A) 90 divided by 22.5 = 4
8.75 divided by 4 = 2.1875 or 2 7/32''.
(B) 90 divided by 10 = 9
8.75 divided by 9 = .9722 or approximately 31/32''.

A chart could now be made of the travel figures for the most common bend angles and different pipe sizes for the bender being used.

Another approach is to divide the travel for 90° (8.75) by 90 to find the travel per degree.

$$8.75 \div 90 = .0972$$

The travel per degree (.0972) can now be multiplied times the desired angle to find the total travel.

EXAMPLE: Find total travel for a 17° bend.
Angle X Travel Per Degree = Total Travel
17 X .0972 = 1.652 or approximately 1 5/8'' Total Travel

Once the travel has been determined, angle bends of less than 90° are achieved by accurate marking and monitoring conduit travel into the bender regardless of whether the bender is level or on a level surface.

PROBLEMS:
1. Ninety degree travel is 10 5/8". Find the travel for (A) 15° (B) 30°.
2. Ninety degree travel is 8 7/8". Find the travel for (A) 60° (B) 45°.

Finding Total Pipe Length Required

All pipe layout techniques described in the EMT section may be used for bending rigid conduit with "CHICAGO" type benders (or any other kind of bender — mechanical or hydraulic).

In most bending jobs the conduit will have more than one bend and the pipe cannot be placed in a power threading machine, and the final cutting, reaming, and threading must be done by hand. Not only a dirty job, but one disliked by most electricians.

This hand work can be eliminated if the total pipe length required for a given job can be determined first. A straight length of pipe can then be measured, cut, reamed and threaded in the "mule" (mule is a term used for free standing power threading machines). The pipe is then marked and bent.

Another situation where it is more convenient to cut, ream, and thread before bending is when the pipe pile and threading equipment are located some distance from the bender.

A new term "GAIN" will be needed to determine total length of pipe required for a given series of bends.

"Gain" is the amount of pipe that is gained by bending on a radius rather than at right angles (Fig. 79).

Fig. 79

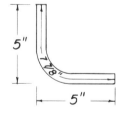

From Fig. 79, we see that the straight line distance totals 10" (5" + 5") but the actual pipe required is only 7 7/8". The difference then is gain. 10" minus 7 7/8" = Gain = 2 1/8".

Gain will vary with each size pipe and type of bender being used.

Gain can be determined mathematically (to be discussed in Hydraulic Bending Section), but for "CHICAGO" bending, gain values should be found by bending scrap pipe.

To find gain for a given pipe size and given bender:

1. Select and measure a straight section of scrap pipe.

2. Place in bender and bend 90° stub.

3. Remove from bender and measure "STUB" and "LEG" length (leg length is measured from the end of the remaining conduit to back of the bend (Fig. 80).

Fig. 80

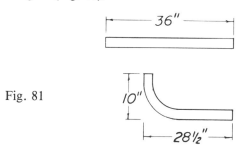

4. Add stub and leg lengths together and subtract original pipe length. The remainder is gain (Fig. 81).

Fig. 81

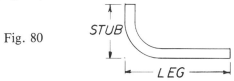

Stub (10") + "Leg" (28½") = 38½" Total

Stub + Leg (38½") minus Straight Length (36") = 2½". Gain = 2½".

Consider two examples of typical bending jobs to find total pipe length.

EXAMPLE 1: ½" Rigid Conduit   Gain 2½"

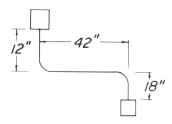

Add all dimensions:

12'' + 42'' + 18'' = 72'' Total Dimension

There are two 90° bends, so there are two gains to consider.

Gain (2½'') X 2 = 5'' Total Gain

Subtract 5'' (total gain) from 72'' (total dimension) = 67'' actual pipe required.

A pipe could now be measured at 67'' cut, reamed, threaded, bending marks located, and pipe bent.

NOTE: For simplicity, all examples and problems will be drawn in one line form, box offsets and thread length will not be included. All measurements are to back of bend.

EXAMPLE 2: ¾'' Rigid Pipe   Gain 3¾''

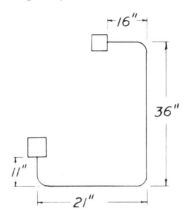

Add all dimensions:

11'' + 21'' + 36'' + 16'' = 84'' Total Dimension

There are three 90° bends.

Gain (3¾'') X 3 = 11¼'' Total Gain

84'' (total dimension) minus 11¼'' (total gain) = 72¾'' actual pipe required.

Now let's add an offset to two bending problems and find total length required.

For 90° bends we subtract gain, for offsets we must add shrink.*

---

*Shrink was covered in the EMT Section.

EXAMPLE 1: ½" Rigid Pipe, Offset 45° bends,
Gain 2½", Shrink 3/8" per inch of rise

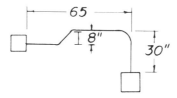

Add all dimensions:
65" + 30" = 95" Total Dimension
Find total shrink:
8" X 3/8" = 3" Total Shrink
Add total shrink to total dimension:
3" + 95" = 98" Adjusted Dimension
Find total gain:
One 90° bend   2½" Total Gain
Subtract total gain from adjusted dimension:
98" minus 2½" = 95½" Total Pipe Required

NOTE: Remember, in reality you must also add an amount for the
threads that enter the boxes.

EXAMPLE 2: ¾" Rigid Pipe, 30° Offset,
Gain 3¾", Shrink ¼" per inch of rise

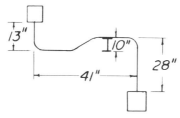

Add all dimensions:
13" + 41" + 28" = 82" Total Dimension
Find total shrink:
10" X ¼" = 2½" Total Shrink
Add total shrink to total dimension:
2½" + 82" = 84½" Adjusted Dimension
Find total gain:
Two 90° bends 2 X 3¾" = 7½" Total Gain
Subtract total gain from adjusted dimension:
84½" minus 7½" = 77" Total Pipe Required

PROBLEMS:

1. Gain 2½"   Shrink 3/8" per inch of rise

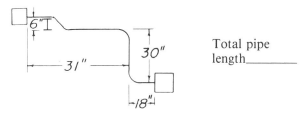

Total pipe
length_____

2. Gain 3¾"   Shrink ¼" per inch of rise

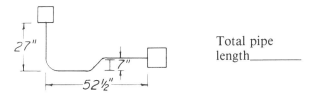

Total pipe
length_____

3. Gain 5 3/8"   Shrink ½" per inch of rise

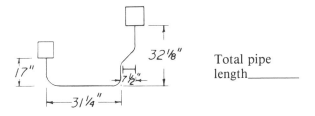

Total pipe
length_____

4. Gain 4¼"   Shrink 3/8" per inch of rise

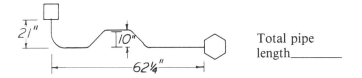

Total pipe
length_____

61

Push-Through Bending

The "CHICAGO" type bender allows us to advance the art of bending. All bends in a given piece of conduit can be made in succession without removing the pipe from the bender. After a bend is made, the pawl is released, the jaw is removed and the pipe is advanced forward to the next bend mark. The jaw is replaced and the bend is made. This technique is called "Push-Through Bending."

To use this technique, all bend marks for a given pipe are placed on the conduit first. This requires additional calculations, but will actually save time (once the electrician is familiar with the procedure and has acquired confidence in the system and himself/herself) and produces more accurate bends. A feeling of pride exists after the pipe has been bent and fits to perfection.

Lets review two terms from previous sections: "take-up" and "gain."

"Take-up" is the distance from the back of the bend to the bending mark and is used to position the bender for accurate 90° bends (Fig. 82).

Fig. 82

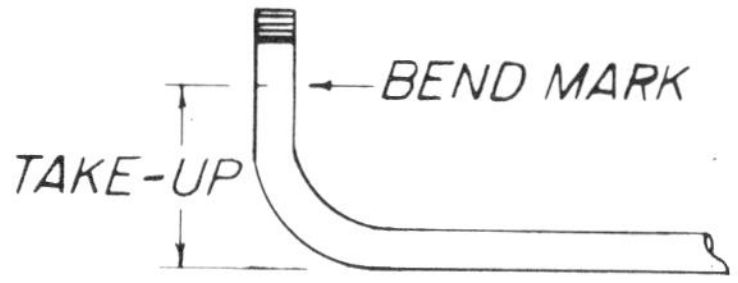

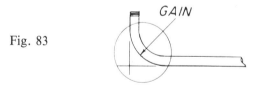

"Gain" is the amount of conduit saved by bending on a radius rather than at right angles (Fig. 83).

Fig. 83

Now let's assume we are bending ½" rigid pipe, the take-up of the bender is 5" and the gain is 2". We need to bend a piece of pipe with a stub of 12" and a leg of 20".

Total pipe length required would be 12" + 20" (stub plus leg) minus 2" (gain) or 30".

To layout the pipe for a 12" stub length, we would subtract 5" take-up and mark the conduit 7" from the end (Fig. 84).

Fig. 84

Bend the 90° stub (Fig. 85).

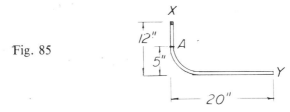

Fig. 85

To find the distance from bend mark A to the end of the leg (Y) we would add 5" (take-up) minus 2" (gain) or 3", plus 20" (leg length) for a total of 23" (Fig. 85). As the pipe is 30" long and bend mark A is 7" from end "X", then A must be 23" from end "Y".

30" minus 7" = 23"

Fig. 86 consists of two right angle bends. Mark A is 5" before the first angle and mark B is 5" before the second angle. The distance from mark A to mark B then is 5" + 47" or 52", which is the same as the back to back distance from angle to angle.

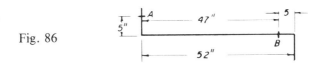

Fig. 86

In Fig. 87 the bends are not at right angles, but bent on a radius. From mark A to B then is 5" minus 2" (gain) or 3", plus 47" or 50".

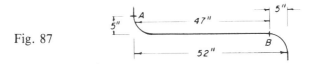

Fig. 87

For double 90° bends, the back-to-back distance minus one gain will be the spacing between marks.

If we can clearly understand how to use take-up and gain, we can locate other bend marks on the pipe from the preceding bend mark.

Do not attempt to go on to the sample problem if you are in doubt about how take-up and gain are being applied. Go back and read the section over for better understanding.

Using ½" rigid pipe and bender with 5" take-up and a gain of 2", let's layout a pipe as indicated in Fig. 88.

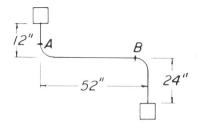

Total pipe required (12" + 52" + 24") minus (2" + 2" for gain) = 84".

Bend mark A will be 12" (stub length) minus 5" (take-up) or 7" from the end of the conduit (Fig. 89).

Fig. 89

Bends A and B have a back-to-back measurement of 52". Bend mark B is located before the bend so the spacing between A and B is 52" minus 2" (one gain) or 50".

This same technique could be used for three or four 90° bends if required. The next problem will have an offset and will use pre-positioning offset Method #1 for layout (covered in EMT section). Method #1 is the only method that will work for push-through bending.

NOTE: For bending rigid conduit on a "CHICAGO" type bender, the constants shown in Table 90 are used.

CONSTANTS	EMT PIPE SIZE			RIGID PIPE SIZE		
ANGLE	1/2"	3/4"	1"	1/2"	3/4"	1"
45°	5"	6 1/4"	7 1/2"	5"	6"	8"
30°	4 1/2"	5 1/2"	6"	4 1/2"	5 1/2"	6 1/2"
22½°	3 1/2"	4 1/4"	4 3/4"	4"	5"	6"
10°	3"	3 1/2"	4"	3"	3 1/2"	4 1/2"

Table 90
Pre-Positioning Offsets Method #1
For "CHICAGO" Benders

Using the same bender and ½" rigid pipe, layout the pipe as required (Fig. 91).

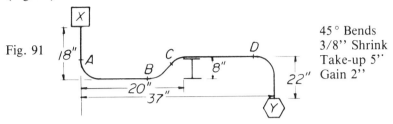

Fig. 91

45° Bends
3/8" Shrink
Take-up 5"
Gain 2"

Total length:
18" + 37" + 22" (total dimensions) + 3" (total shrink) minus 4" (gain) = 76" (Fig. 92).

Fig. 92

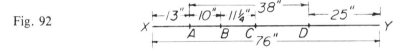

Bend mark A

Stub length 18" minus 5" = 13" from end of pipe (Fig. 92).

The distance from A to B, using Method #1 for pre-determining offset location.

From bend mark A to the back of the bend is 5" (take-up) minus 2" (gain) or 3". The edge of the obstruction is 20" to the back of the bend, so by adding 3" and 20" we locate the obstruction from bend mark A at 23".

The height of the obstruction 8" plus the constant (for 45° bends — ½" rigid pipe) of 5" for a total of 13". This total (13") is subtracted from the distance of the obstruction to bend mark A (23") to locate bend mark B, 10" from A (Fig. 92).

The distance from B to C

Height of obstruction (8") times 45° multiplier (1.4)
8" X 1.4 = 11.2 or 11¼" (Fig. 92).

To locate bend mark D, it is easier to use mark A as a reference. Back-to-back measurement from A to D is 37", minus one gain (2") or 35", shrink must be added to this figure because of the offset. Add 3" (total shrink) to 35" for spacing between A and D of 38" (Fig. 92).

We can, and should, always double check our figures before bending. The best way is to work backwards and add our figures.

Working from point Y to bend mark D is 22" + 5" (take-up) minus 2" (gain) = 25". From D to A is 38" added to 25" = 63". From A to the end of the conduit is 13'' added to 63'' = 76'', the total pipe length.

By making these extra calculations, any mistakes that might have been made, will quickly show up.

The next problem will have a saddle. Review the EMT section covering Pre-determining Saddle Location Method #1. As with offsets, Method #1 must be used for push-through bending.

Layout pipe as indicated. ¾'' rigid pipe, take-up 6'', gain 2¾'' and 45° bends (Fig. 93).

Fig. 93

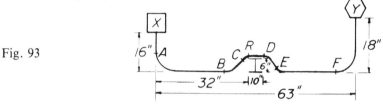

Find total length:

Dimensions (16'' + 63'' + 18'') plus total shrink (height of obstruction twice) 12'' X 3/8'' (4½'') minus total gain (2¾'' + 2¾'') or 5½'' = 96'' (Fig. 94).

Fig. 94

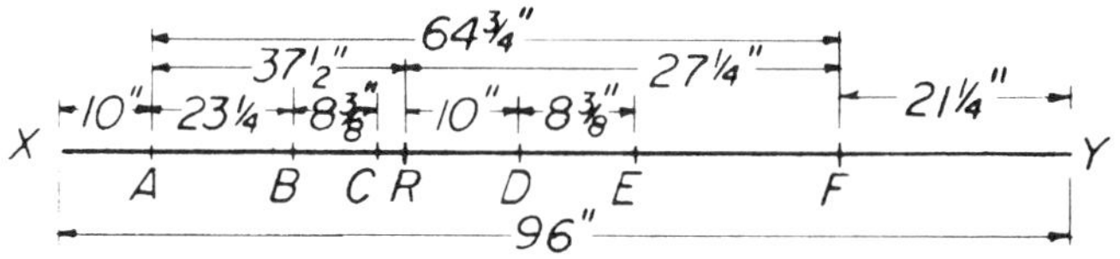

Locate mark A:

Stub (16'') minus take-up (6'') = 10'' from end of pipe (Fig. 94).

The distance from A to B:

From A to back of bend is 6'' (take-up) minus 2¾'' (gain) or 3¼''. The edge of the obstruction is 32'' from the back of the bend, so by adding 3¼'' and 32'' we locate the obstruction from bend A, 35¼''. From this distance we subtract 6'' (height of obstruction) + 6'' (45° constant for ¾'' rigid pipe as found in Table 90) to locate bend mark B.

35¼'' minus 12'' = 23¼'' (Fig.94).

Distance from B to C:

Height of obstruction (6'') times 45° multiplier (1.4) = 8.4'' or approximately 8 3/8'' (Fig. 94).

66

The distance from A to R:

We have already located the edge of the obstruction from A (35¼"). Now add shrink for ½ of the saddle (6 X 3/8 = 18/8 or 2¼") to the total distance from A to the obstruction (35¼") to locate R 37½" from A (Fig. 94).

Distance from R to D:

Measure over the width of the obstruction (10") (Fig. 94).

Distance from D to E:

Same as B to C 8 3/8" (Fig. 94).

Locate mark F:

Mark F may be located from A or R.

From R to F:

The back-to-back measurement of bend A to F is 63", it is 32" from the back of bend A to the obstruction so it must be 31" from the obstruction to the back of bend F. R indicated the edge of the obstruction, so 31" (distance from R to back of bend F) + 2¼" (shrink for ½ the saddle) = 33¼" minus 6" take-up = 27¼" (Fig. 94).

From A to F:

Back-to-back measurement from bend A to bend F is 63". 63" (distance) + 4½" (total shrink) minus 2¾" (one gain) = 64¾" (Fig. 94).

To double check our figures:

From end of pipe (Y), 18" (stub) plus 6" (take-up) minus 2¾" (gain) = 21¼" to bend mark F. Bend mark F to bend mark A is 64¾", sub total 21¼" + 64¾" = 86". From bend mark A to the end of the pipe (X) is 10". Sub total 86" + 10" = 96" total pipe. Also note that A to R (37½") plus R to F (27¼") totals 64¾" which is the same distance as A to F.

This may all seem very complicated at first, but with a little practice you will be able to do it rather easily. Again the key is complete understanding of take-up, gain, shrink and offset constant values.

PROBLEMS:

Find total pipe length needed and layout bend marks as required.

1. 45° offset, ½" rigid pipe, 5¼" take-up, 2 3/8"gain.

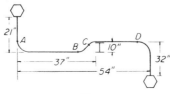

2. 6" take-up, 3 3/8" gain

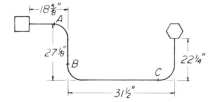

3. 45° saddle, ¾" rigid pipe, 6½" take-up, 3¼" gain.

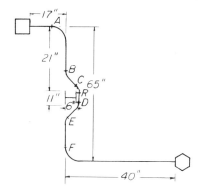

For Pre-Positioning Saddles:

When using "CHICAGO" type bending equipment an adjustment must be made if very close fitting saddles are required. The adjustment in the layout is necessary because the bend will not actually start at the bend mark but back in the bending shoe (Fig. 95).

The amount that must be considered will vary with different types of benders. Scrap pipe can be bent and the distance from the bend mark to actual start of bend determined. This distance is then deducted from the width of the obstruction. Fig. 96 shows how the saddle will fit if no adjustment is made, while Fig. 97 shows the fit if an amount is deducted.

Fig. 95

Bend mark at start of bending shoe _____

Pipe actually bends back in bending shoe

Distance from R to C is
width of obstruction

Distance from R to
C = Width of obstruction
minus correction factor

Fig. 96

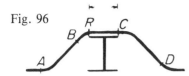

Fig. 97

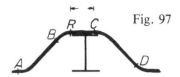

Finished saddle without deduction   Finished saddle with deduction

Three Bend Saddles Using "Chicago" Benders:

1. Bend scrap pipe to 45° and mark shoe for center of bend (as shown in Fig. 98).

a. ALL bends (45° and the two 22½°) will be made using this mark.

2. Multiplier will be 3.

NOTE: Multiplier of 2½" is only used with **hand bending** EMT or rigid pipe.

EXAMPLE: 8" Diameter pipe.

8" X 3 = 24"

Locate bend mark A and place marks B and C 24" either side of A.

Place conduit in bender lining mark on shoe (center of bend indicating mark) with bend mark B. Bend a 22½° bend, rotate pipe 180° advance to bend mark A, bend a 45° bend, rotate pipe 180°, advance to bend mark C, bend a 22½° bend to complete the saddle.

Fig. 98

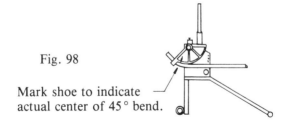

Mark shoe to indicate
actual center of 45° bend.

General "CHICAGO" Bending Tips:

1. An engineers rule marked in hundreds will simplify formula bending by eliminating the need to convert to fractions.

2. When minimum length stubs are being bent, the shoe tends to creep and deforms the end of the conduit and threads. Screwing a coupling on the pipe stops the shoe from creeping forward and protects the threads.

3. When bending offsets, the front of the bender can be temporarily elevated for clearance requirements.

4. Most bender shoes are made of cast aluminum and are easily pitted and gouged if foreign material gets between the shoe and the pipe. Keep the pipe clean and shoes wiped down for longer shoe life.

5. When the remaining pipe length is not long enough to reach the roller or pipe support, a larger diameter conduit can be slid over the pipe being bent to complete the bend (Fig. 99), or if the pipe has threads, screw on a coupling and short piece of scrap pipe.

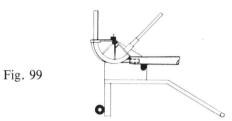

Fig. 99

6. Segment and concentric bending of smaller sizes of pipe can be performed with the "CHICAGO" type bender.

Bend a scrap piece of pipe and measure from center of bend to front of bending shoe.

Use this measurement to adjust the start mark using Segment and Concentric Bending procedure as described in Chapters 15, 16 and 17.

NOTE: For matching bends in sizes ½", ¾" and 1", bend all pipes with the 1" shoe.

HYDRAULIC BENDERS 14

For bending larger size conduit the Hydraulic Bender is indispensable. Only by the addition of the hydraulic pump and cylinder to a bender frame is the necessary power available for bending rigid conduit up to 6" trade size.

The typical completely assembled hydraulic bender as shown in Fig. 100 not only gives the electrician extended bending capability, but also requires additional responsibility. Hydraulic bending equipment represents a large initial investment of money and the bender must be properly cared for if it is to last and give the service necessary to justify the cost.

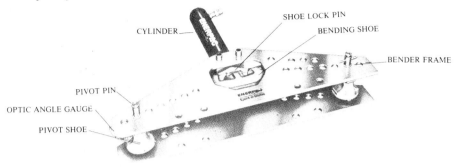

Fig. 100
Courtesy — Enerpac, Co.

The bender frame, pivot shoes and bending shoes will require little more than occasional wiping down to remove the dirt and oil film. The pump, cylinder and hydraulic hoses, however, will demand more attention.

Newer model benders come with quick-disconnect couplers on the pump, cylinder and hoses. Each coupler end comes with a dust cover (Fig. 101). These dust covers must be in place when the bender is disassembled to keep dirt and dust out of the couplers. Failure to keep the couplers clean will result in damage to the "O" Rings (hydraulic pressure depends on the "O" Ring seating properly).

Female Coupler with Dust Cap   Male Coupler with Dust Cap

Fig. 101
Courtesy — Enerpac, Co.

The pump, whether hand or electrically operated, should have the fluid level checked periodically. Low fluid pressure will keep the pump from developing its rated hydraulic pressure. When level is low and fluid must be added, use only approved hydraulic oil. Ordinary oil will cause damage to the pump assembly (Fig. 102).

71

Fig. 102
Courtesy — Enerpac, Co.

Hydraulic benders have two types of bending shoes, One-shot and Segment.

The one-shot shoe has a full 90° radius (Fig. 103). The conduit can be formed around the shoe to a full 90° bend without collapsing the walls of the pipe. One-shot benders require no new bending techniques. The take-up is figured to the center of the bend and the bender shoe will have an indicating mark at its center. If take-up values are not listed on the bender frame or bender storage case, scrap pipe can be bent and take-up figures found. All the methods and layout techniques discussed for EMT and Rigid can be used with a hydraulic bender and one shot shoes. Offsets will have to be adjusted (less angle of bend) so the spacing between the bend marks is far enough apart to allow the first bend to be rolled 180° and advanced enough to clear the pivot shoe.

Fig. 103

Segment shoes are shorter and have little radius or a radius far less than 90° (Fig. 104). 90 degree bends cannot be made in one operation as the conduit walls will collapse. Bends then must be made in several steps (as few as 4, and as many as 30) to form a smooth radius. The segment shoe allows pipe to be bent to larger size radii.

Fig. 104

Segment shoes are used for Concentric Bending (bending several conduits with increasing or decreasing radii). One-shot shoes can be used for segment bending, but are not as convenient. Concentric bending is covered in detail later in the text.

Accurate bending of large conduit is possible, but requires practice, patience and ability. With few exceptions, all formulas and bending techniques discussed to this point will apply.

Bending Tips for Rigid Aluminum

Aluminum conduit is available in all trade sizes, ½" through 6". It is light weight, corrosion resistant and has low ground impedance.

It is, however, difficult to bend consistently and accurately. Two pipes out of the same bundle will act differently when bent. Even if two pipes are bent using the same layout, they don't always come out the same. Don't be discouraged, this is the nature of the metal, and it can't be helped.

A one-shot bending shoe will dig-in and score the pipe and where the pipe rides on the pivot shoe is also prone to wrinkling and scoring. Applying petroleum jelly (Vaseline) to the shoes will allow the pipe to slide without the shoes digging in. The Vaseline will also make it easier to remove the conduit when the bend is complete.

LAYOUT FOR SEGMENT BENDING   15

Segment bending will require some new information and bending techniques.

Segment bends, as mentioned earlier require more than one bend to complete a 90° stub. As many as 30 bends may be used and this would require 30 bend marks.

The first step in segment bending is to determine the size radius at which the pipe is to be bent. The larger the radius, the easier wire pulling will be. Space requirements and installation location will also be a factor that will govern the radius of a given pipe.

The National Electrical Code® gives the minimum bend radius for rigid pipe. A "rule-of-thumb" to determine the minimum bending radius is 6 to 8 times the trade size of the conduit.

Notice in Fig. 105 that the bent portion of a 90° bend makes up ¼ of the circumference of a circle, also note that the radius is ½ the diameter. The formula: Circumference = 3.14* X Diameter is used to find the circumference of a circle.

Fig. 105

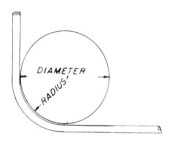

Then to find only ¼ of the circumference (amount of bent pipe) the formula can be changed to read: ¼ Circumference = 1.57 (½ of 3.14) X Radius (½ of diameter).

The ¼ circumference or the amount of bent pipe in a 90° bend is called the "Developed Length." Stated yet another way, developed length is the amount of straight pipe required to bend a given size radius (Fig. 106).

Developed length for a 90° bend = 1.57 X Radius

Fig. 106

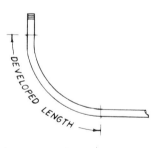

As indicated in Fig. 107, the radius is measured on the inside of the bend. The radius plus the outside diameter** of the pipe is just like "take-up" as described in the preceding sections.

---

*3.14 is substituted for the Greek letter ⅄(Pi) which is the ratio of the circumference of a circle to its diameter.

**Complete list of pipe dimensions are in the back of the book.

This amount (Radius + Outside Diameter) subtracted from the desired stub length will give us the start mark. The start mark is used for layout only and is **not** a bend mark.

Fig. 107

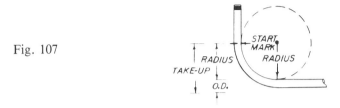

EXAMPLE: To locate the start mark (used for reference only, not a bend mark) from the end of the conduit for a 48" stub in a 4" conduit with a 22" radius, simply subtract the radius (22") plus the outside diameter for 4" rigid pipe (4½") from desired stub length of 48". This gives us a start mark of 21½" as shown in Fig. 108.

Fig. 108

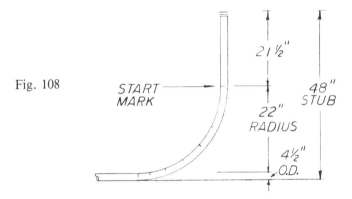

The start mark as well as all other bending marks should go at least half way around the pipe. If marks are too small, they will be covered by the bending shoe and create problems when the bending is started.

As more than one bend must be made to complete the 90° stub, the next step then is to determine the number of bends.

Fig. 109a and Fig. 109b are exaggerated, but serve to illustrate a point. The more bends — the smoother and uniform the radius.

Fig. 109a

Fig. 109b

Examples of number of bends and degree per bend for 90° segment bending are as follows:

Number of bends	Degree per bend
15	6
18	5
20	4.5
30	3

Normally the degrees per bend should not be less than 3° (30 shots) nor more than 6° (15 shots) for smooth, even radius bends. Any degree between 3° and 6° of course may be used.

Remember the more bends the smoother the 90° stub and the easier wire pulling will be.

Once you have decided on the number of bends to be used, the number is divided into the developed length (the amount of straight pipe needed to bend a given radius) to give us the spacing between bend marks (Fig. 110).

Fig. 110

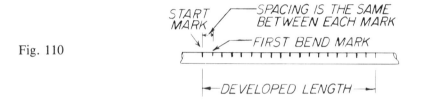

$$\text{Developed length} = \frac{\text{Spacing between marks}}{\text{Number of bends}}$$

EXAMPLE: Determine spacing between marks for a 22" radius bent in 20 shots.

NOTE: "Shots" is another term applied to bends. (20 shots is the same as 20 bends)

Developed length = 1.57 X Radius (22")
1.57 X 22" = 34.54" Developed length

Developed length (34.54") divided by number of shots (20) = 1.727" or approximately 1¾" spacing between marks.

Now that the new terms have been covered, let's put it all together and layout two segment bends.

PROBLEM #1: Layout a 3" pipe bent 90° to a 42" stub with a 24" radius. (bend in 20 shots)

1. Find the developed length:
Developed length = 1.57 X 24" (radius)
Developed length = 37.68"

76

2. Determine location of start mark.

Start mark = Desired stub length 42" minus radius (24") + Outside diameter of pipe (3.5")

42" minus (24" + 3.5") = 42" minus 27.5"

Start mark = 14.5"

3. Spacing between marks:

37.68" (developed length) divided by 20 (number of shots) = 1.884 or approximately 1 7/8" spacing between marks.

Starting 14½" from end of conduit, place 20 marks spaced 1 7/8" apart (Fig. 111).

Fig. 111

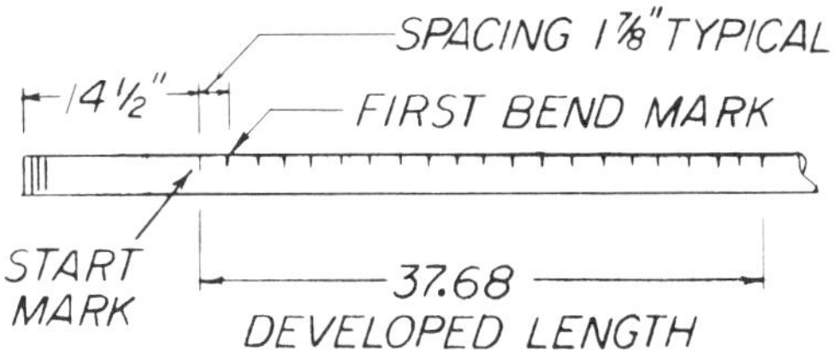

4. Conduit is placed in bender and bent 20 times, 4½ ° per bend (4½ ° X 20 = 90°).

NOTE: Complete bending instructions are covered in the next chapter.

PROBLEM #2: Layout 4" pipe bent 90° to a 51" stub and a 30" radius. (15 shots)

1. Find developed length:

Developed length = 1.57 X 30" (radius)

Developed length = 47.1"

2. Locate start mark:

Start mark = Desired stub height (51") minus radius (30") + O.D. of pipe (4.5")

51" minus (30" + 4.5")

51" minus 34.5" = 16.5"

Locate start mark 16½" from end of pipe.

3. Find spacing between marks:

Spacing = Developed length (47.1") divided by shots (15)

47.1" divided by 15 = 3.14 or approximately 3 1/8"

4. Starting at the start mark (16½"), place 15 marks 3 1/8" apart on the conduit.

Pipe is now ready to bend.

PROBLEMS:

1. Find start mark and spacing for a 2½'' Conduit-24'' Radius-62'' Stub-20 Shots.

2. Find start mark and spacing for a 4'' conduit-40'' Radius-68'' Stub-30 Shots.

Of the several methods of layout in use for segment bending, the author has elected to use the one he feels is easiest to remember. The success of the method described, as with any method or technique, depends on the electrician's mechanical ability and the equipment being used.

NOTE: No matter which bending method is used, if for some reason your results are consistently high or low, make certain you are performing the bending procedures correctly, then adjust your layout to compensate.

It is extremely important that you check your developing stub length and angle of bend when you have 4 or 5 shots left. Corrections and/or adjustments can be easily made during these last few bends.

If the stub is coming up long, bend more degrees per shot to bring stub to 90°. If stub is coming up short, lengthen the spacing between shots to pick-up the necessary added stub length.

NOTE: A wallet sized cut-out card with the formula for segment bending is located on the last page of this book.

SEGMENT BENDING TECHNIQUES   16

Now that the procedure to layout the conduit with bending marks is understood, the next step is bending.

As segment bending requires several small angle bends to complete a 90° stub, some method to measure the amount of bend in degrees will be required.

This can be done basically four ways:

1. Bend Degree Protractor

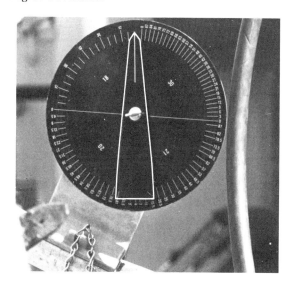

This is a device that hooks onto the pipe being bent. The circular face is divided into four sections (18, 20, 21 and 30 shots) and is capable of being rotated to whichever scale is to be used. The indicating pointer is weighted and swings free. To use this device:

(a) The conduit is leveled and secured (pipe vise or other means).

(b) The face is rotated to the desired scale that corresponds to the number of shots being used.

(c) The scale is "fine" adjusted so the pointer is on O.

(d) The pipe is bent until the pointer reaches the first mark. (Bend a little past to compensate for spring back, release pressure and check pointer. Only a few bends will be needed and you will find just how much you must bend past the mark for spring back.)

(e) Pipe is moved forward in the bender to the second bend mark and bent until the pointer reaches the second mark on the protractor face. (Again bend past for spring back)

(f) The conduit is moved to the third mark and the pipe is bent so the pointer is at the third mark (after allowing for spring back). This procedure is followed at each bend mark until the 90° stub has been achieved.

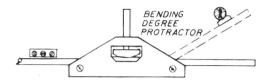

Fig. 112

Pipe is leveled and bender is in a vertical position.

NOTE: It is a good idea to check developing stub length before the last few bends are made. Make spacing corrections as required. (Shorten spacing if stub is coming up short.) If stub length is reached before the stub is plumb, don't bend at any of the remaining marks, move pipe in bender and bend at the start mark. This will bring the stub to plumb without adding to the stub length.

2. Magnetic Angle Finder

Pipe must be kept level and bent vertically (Fig. 113)

Fig. 113

Pipe is leveled and bender is in vertical position.

When a magnetic angle finder is used, care must be taken with each bend as a very small error multiplied 15 to 30 times is a LARGE error.

To use the angle finder:

(a) Level conduit and place angle finder on stub end.

(b) The angle finder will indicate degrees of each bend (as determined by number of shots i.e. 20 shots each bend 4.5°)

(c) Pipe is bent until angle finder indicates just past the desired degree of bend. By bending past the actual amount or angle of bend we will be able to allow for spring back. Release hydraulic pressure, if the right amount of overbend was made to allow for spring back, the angle finder should read the desired angle of bend. If you bent too much for spring back or allowed too little, make the adjustment on the next bend. In two or three bends you will find just the right amount to over bend at each mark to allow for spring back.

(d) Move pipe to second bend mark. Bend at this mark until the next setting on the angle finder (allowing for spring back) is indicated by the angle finder pointer.

EXAMPLE: First bend 4½°
Second bend 9°
Third bend 13½°, etc.

(e) Pipe is bent at each successive bend mark using angle finder to indicate proper degree of bend.

NOTE: Again check developing stub length before bending last few bends. Adjust spacing or amount of bend as required.

Amount of Travel Method

(Pipe may be bent in any position.)

This method is very similar to the Amount of Travel Method discussed in the "CHICAGO" bending section. It varies only in the method in which the travel figures are derived.

To find the amount of theoretical travel for a 90° bend, proceed as follows:

(a) Set up bender with pivot shoes in proper holes for conduit that is to be bent.

(b) Measure the distance (D) center-to-center between the pivot shoe pins (Fig. 114).

Fig. 114

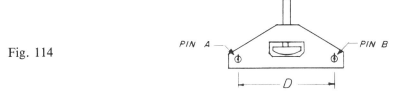

D-distance from center of pin A to center of pin B

(c) The plunger (also called the ram) will have to travel half this distance to bend a full 90° stub (Fig. 115).

Fig. 115

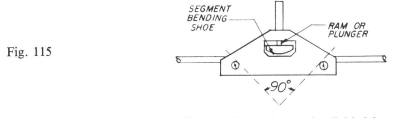

(d) Travel per shot then is ½ distance from pin to pin divided by number of shots.

81

EXAMPLE: Distance from center of pins is 24" and pipe is to be bent in 18 shots.

Travel per shot = ½ the distance from center of pins (12") divided by number of shots (18).

½ Distance (12") divided by Number of shots (18) = .666 or approximately 21/32"

Travel per shot = 21/32"

Bending with this method we will follow a slightly different procedure.

The center of the bending shoe is placed on the first bending mark (not the start mark) and the pump is actuated until 21/32" of ram travel is measured (Fig. 116). **Do NOT** allow for spring back with this method.

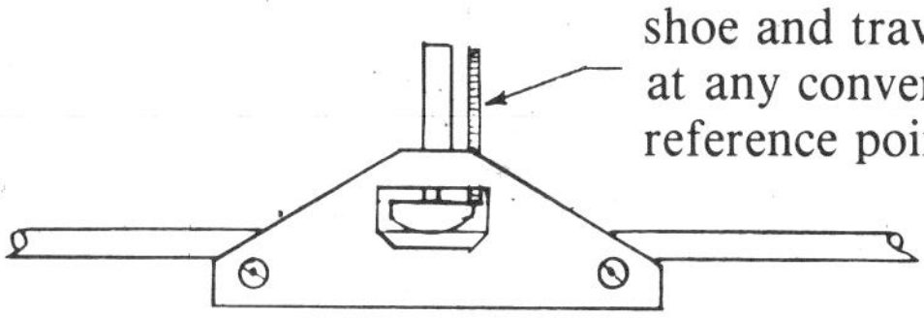

Fig. 116

Rule is placed on bender shoe and travel read at any convenient reference point.

The pipe is moved to the next mark and the pump is accuated until another 21/32" of ram travel have been measured. Continue to move the pipe and measure ram travel.

As you approach the last few marks (4 or 5), check both the developing stub length and angle of bend. Spacing and/or amount of travel can be adjusted on these last marks to bring the stub on the "money" or for final truing.

NOTE: Once you have found the amount of travel for 90°, we can also find the amount of travel for any other angle for offsets, kicks, etc.

Divide 90° travel by 90 and multiply by the desired bend angle.

EXAMPLE: If 90° travel is 12". What is the travel for 22½°?

12" divided by 90 = .1333"
.1333" X 22.5 = 2.999" or 3"

4. Number of Pumps Method

(Pipe may be bent in any position.)

This method depends on the fact that a given hydraulic pump will produce the same amount of bend for a given number of pumps of the handle, but does not take into account that the number of pumps will change with a change in fluid level, and condition of the pump and "O" rings.

EXAMPLE: If it takes 40 pumps to bend a 90° stub, it should only take 20 pumps to achieve 45°, 10 pumps for 22½°, 2 pumps for 4½°, etc.

As you can see this method should work very well, but will require additional time to determine pump/degree values. But this can be offset by not having to measure ram travel at each bend as required by amount of travel method.

Use the same procedure for bending as outlined in Amount of Travel Method. Check developing stub length and degree of bend prior to bending the last few shots. Use these remaining shots for final adjustments in stub length and truing the 90° bend.

NOTE:　Use any one of the four methods that is most convenient, but bear in mind that extreme care and attention to detail is required in all methods. A small amount of error at each bend will compound itself and accuracy in bending will be impossible to achieve.

To make hydraulic bending easier, a bending table, either a commercial model (Fig. 117) or one constructed on the job is a necessity. The table will hold the conduit and the bender, making leveling and plumbing easier and produce more accurate bends. The table will also eliminate the need to continually "wrestle" the conduit and bender.

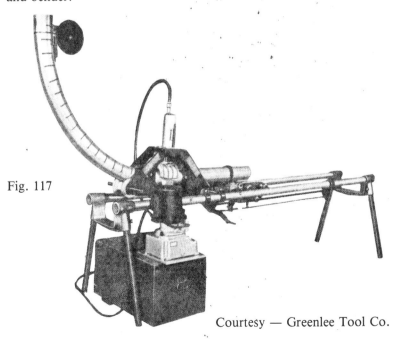

Fig. 117

Courtesy — Greenlee Tool Co.

In the event a table is not available or impracticable due to job conditions, an indispensable bending aid is the "wow-watcher". Figs. 118a and b show devices that are easily fabricated on the job and are used for leveling the conduit to eliminate wows and dog-legs (see glossary of terms) as the conduit is moved in the bender. The wow-watcher is a handy device for offsets and multiple bend pipe jobs.

Fig. 118a

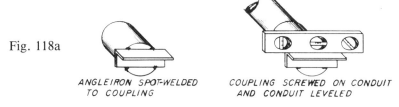

ANGLE IRON SPOT-WELDED
TO COUPLING

COUPLING SCREWED ON CONDUIT
AND CONDUIT LEVELED

If no welder is available, an alternate method is to clamp uni-strut onto the conduit being bent (Fig. 118b)

Fig. 118b

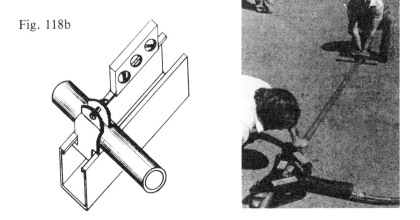

Although not as mechanically sound, a hacksaw blade may be used (Fig. 119). Saw a slot across the coupling and insert a sawblade, the slot is then peened to hold the blade fast.

Fig. 119

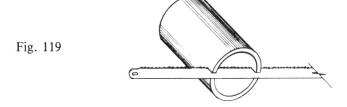

Segment Offsets

(and other bends under 90°)

To bend offsets or any other bend of less than 90° will require little new information.

We will need to determine the radius, find the developed length and spacing between bend marks much the same way we did for 90° stubs.

We can find the developed length by multiplying the Radius X Degree of bend X .0175 (1.57 divided by 90).

Developed length (less than 90° bend) = Radius X Degree of bend X .0175

EXAMPLE: Find the developed length for a 30° bend with a 20" radius.

Radius (20") X Degree of bend (30°) X .0175 = 10.5" Developed length

Next we need to determine spacing.

Remember the rule for smooth bends, (not less than 3° nor more than 6° bends) let's select 5°. It will take 6 bends of 5° to make our 30° bend (6 X 5° = 30°).

Number of Bends (6) divided into developed length (10.5") = 1.75" or 1 ¾" spacing between bend marks (Fig. 120).

Fig. 120

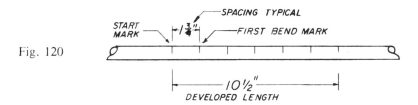

Consider a typical offset bending assignment, an 8" offset in 3" pipe:

1. Determine radius: If space is no problem, 8 times trade size of conduit (3") = 24".

2. Determine angle of offset: (smaller bends make easier wire pulling) Assuming space is no problem, let's bend 20⁰ bends.

3. Find Developed length:
Radius (24") X Degree of bend (20°) X .0175 = 8.4" Developed length.

4. Number of shots: For smoothness of bend, use 4°, 5 shots X 4° will give us our 20° offset bend.

85

5. Spacing between shots:
Number of shots (5) divided into Developed Length (8.4") = 1.68 or approximately 1 5/8" (to nearest 1/8").
6. Spacing between offset bends:
Height of offset 8" X 2.92 (multiplier for 20°) = 23.39" or approximately 23 3/8" between the start marks.
7. Layout pipe and bend: (Fig. 121)

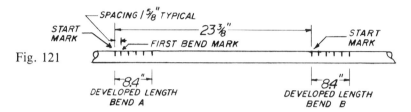

Fig. 121

It should be noted at this point that all multipliers and shrink values listed earlier in the text may be applied to segment bending regardless of pipe size.

Bending offsets over 30° at larger than normal radius may end up too long when shrink is used and the pipe is cut and threaded before bending. This is caused by gain in the two bends.

Although correction factors will depend on the equipment being used, the chart below should be close enough for most equipment.

ANGLE OF OFFSET BENDS	30°	37½°	45°	60°
CORRECTION FACTOR	.0124	.0212	.0430	.1076

To apply the correction factor:

Locate correction factor under angle of offset bend. Multiply this value times radius of bend. This product is deducted from total pipe length after all other standard calculations have been made.

EXAMPLE:

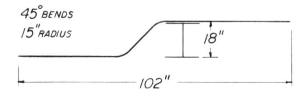

Total shrink: Height of obstruction (18") X 3/8" = 6¾"

Total pipe length: Total dimension (102") + Total shrink (6¾") = 108¾".

Under the 45° column is a correction factor of .0430. This value (.0430) is multiplied times the radius of the bend (15").

$$\begin{array}{r} .0430 \\ \underline{X\ 15} \\ 0.654 \end{array}\text{ or approximately 5/8"}$$

5/8" is subtracted from total pipe length.

108¾" minus 5/8" = 108 1/8"

This correction factor as indicated is very general and may have to be adjusted up or down as you find necessary.

Segment Saddles

Regular saddles will be bent as outlined earlier in the text. A saddle is simply two offsets, so using the previous information and that just covered in Segment Offsets, bending hydraulically should pose no problem.

The three bend saddle bent hydraulically, must be changed a bit and bent as two complete offsets tight together. This type saddle is still used primarily for bridging round obstructions (Fig. 122a).

Fig. 122a

The angle selected for the bends should be as small as possible to leave plenty of straight pipe between bends 1 and 2 and also between bends 3 and 4. The minimum length of straight pipe required will be determined by the distance from the center of the bending shoe to the pivot shoe. If the length is not long enough you will take bend out of Bend 1 when trying to bend at Bend 2.

Bend 1 and 2 are identical to 3 and 4, so the layout is also identical (122b).

Fig. 122b

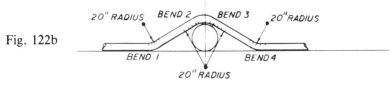

Concentric 90° Bends

Concentric is defined as having a common center or axis. Notice in Fig. 123 that starting from the inside pipe, each pipe has an increasing radius.

Concentric pipe work requires no new layout techniques, only increasing the radius of the next pipe to maintain even spacing.

The layout for concentric pipe is quite simple then.

The radius of the first pipe is decided upon and the bend marks which were discussed previously are laid out for a segment bent 90° stub.

The second radius is found by adding to the radius of the first pipe, the O.D. of first pipe, and the desired spacing between pipes.

EXAMPLE: (Fig. 123)

Radius of first pipe   24"
O.D. of first pipe   3.5"
Spacing between pipes   2"
Radius of second pipe   24" + 3.5" + 2" = 29.5" or 29½"

Once the developed length of the second radius is found, the spacing between marks can be determined. The start mark must be the same distance from the end of the second pipe as it was for the first pipe (Fig. 123). This will be true for each additional pipe as well.

The spacing will increase between marks as the radius of the pipes increase. This is due to increasing developed length.

The pipes in Fig. 123 are all laid out for 15 shots.

Fig. 123

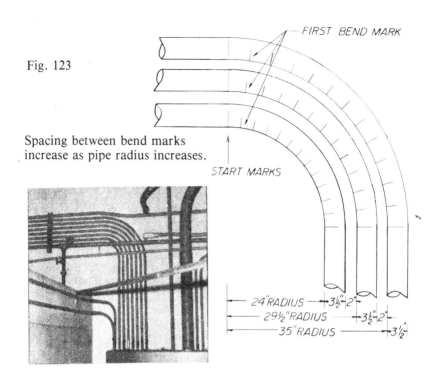

FIRST BEND MARK

Spacing between bend marks increase as pipe radius increases.

START MARKS

24" RADIUS — 3½" 2"
29½" RADIUS — 3½" 2"
35" RADIUS — 3½"

Gain = 2 X Radius minus Developed Length

When bending several concentric pipes, the spacing between bend marks will increase with each additional pipe. If the spacing becomes too wide, the radius will not appear smooth. To compensate, increase the number of shots (which will make the marks closer together) whenever needed. The start mark, however, must remain the same as the previous pipes.

PROBLEM:

Layout for concentric 90° bends.
First pipe 2"-18" Radius-48" Stub
Second pipe 3½"
Third pipe 2½"
Spacing between pipes 2". All pipes bent in 20 shots.

First pipe: Find
(a) Developed length
(b) Spacing between shots
(c) Start mark from end of conduit

Second pipe: Find
(a) Radius
(b) Developed length
(c) Spacing between shots
(d) Start mark from end of conduit
Third pipe: Find
(a) Radius
(b) Developed length
(c) Spacing between shots
(d) Start mark from end of conduit

Concentric Offsets:

Use the same procedure as for 90° stubs. Increase the radius of the second pipe, an amount equal to radius of first pipe plus O.D. of first pipe plus spacing desired between pipes (Fig. 124).

This applies to ends A-1 and B-1, notice, however, the ends A-2 and B-2 are in reverse order.

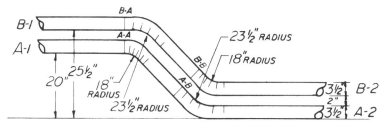

Fig. 124

This layout will be necessary if perfect fitting parallel run conduits is to be achieved.

Spacing between bend marks A-A and A-B is found as with any offset: Desired offset height (20'') X Offset multiplier for 30° (2) = 40'' between bends A-A and A-B. As the offset will be bent using two different radii the spacing (40'') must be from CENTER of developed length A-A to CENTER of developed length A-B (Fig. 125).

Although pipe B is 25½'' from the surface, due to spacing above pipe A, it must also have a 20'' offset height. 25½'' minus O.D. Pipe A (3½'') minus spacing (2'') = 20''.

Both pipes are then laid out with the same start mark, but with the bend radius being reversed.

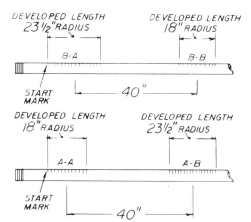

DEVELOPED LENGTH
23½"RADIUS

B-A

DEVELOPED LENGTH
18"RADIUS

B-B

START
MARK

40"

Fig. 125

DEVELOPED LENGTH
18"RADIUS

A-A

DEVELOPED LENGTH
23½"RADIUS

A-B

START
MARK

40"

Although the examples used to explain offset bending had several shots per bend, it should be clearly understood that fewer shots can be used. Successful offsets can be made with only 2 or 3 shots per bend.

It is the author's contention that with offsets, 90° bends or any other segment bends, that the additional time spent bending smoother radius bends (more shots) is gained back when the conductors are pulled into the completed raceway.

Fig. 126 shows two concentric offsets as just explained. Bending parallel offsets in this manner is rewarding from a technical standpoint, but is, however, time consuming.

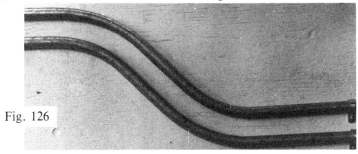

Fig. 126

Parallel offsets of different pipe sizes can still be bent and aligned perfectly if all pipes are bent with the same one-shot shoe. This will work with 2'', 1½'' and 1¼'' pipe sizes and depending on the manufacturer and the ductility of the pipe 2½'', 2'', 1½'' and 1¼'' can all be bent on the same 2½'' one-shot shoe. 3'', 3½'' and 4'' can usually be bent on the 4'' shoe. Again it will depend on the ductility of the pipe and you will just have to experiment with the different sizes of pipe and shoes to find out what will work.

Refer to Chapter 8 (Parallel Offsets) for more detailed information.

INTERMEDIATE METAL CONDUIT (IMC)

Intermediate Metal Conduit as the name implies is intermediate (between) EMT and Rigid. Fig. 127 shows a comparison of wall thickness. Even with its reduced wall thickness IMC is cut, reamed and threaded with standard pipe equipment.

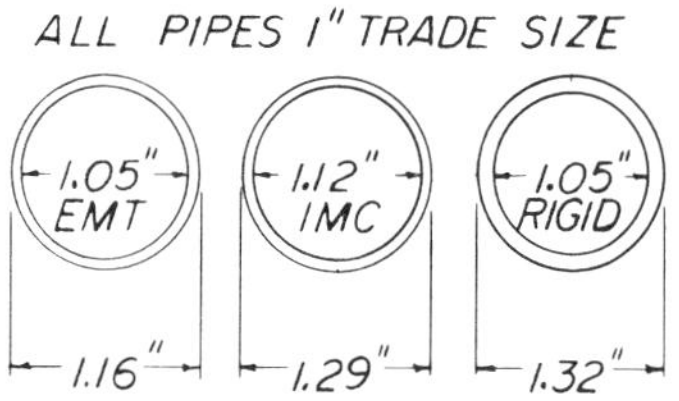

Fig. 127

ALL PIPES 1" TRADE SIZE

IMC is available in trade sizes: ½", ¾", 1", 1¼", 1½", 2", 2½", 3", 3½" and 4". Standard length is 10' including the coupling.

National Electrical Code® Article 345, governs the use and installation of IMC.

Bending IMC

With the difference in O.D., different wall thickness and the hardness of the metal that gives it its strength, support must be provided to the sides of the conduit.

Hand Bending: ½", ¾" and 1" trade sizes can be accomplished with IMC hand benders, Rigid hand benders (not Hickeys) or the next size larger EMT bender.

Hickey bending of IMC is not recommended. The design of the Hickey does not give the required support to the sides of the conduit. If there is no other way available, IMC can be bent with a Hickey, but must be "inched" and done with care.

"CHICAGO" type benders, using existing rigid shoes will bend IMC trade sizes ½" through 1¼". Some types will bend up to 1½" (See chart on page 108 for specific manufacturers).

Electric Benders are available that will bend ½" through 2" IMC (Fig. 70a page 51)

Hydraulic Benders are available to bend 1¼" through 4" IMC, in some cases this will require conversion attachment kits for existing model benders. There are also new models that are designed expressly for IMC.

NOTE: Refer to IMC bending chart on page 108 for partial list of IMC benders and bending equipment available.

RIGID PVC (Polyvinyl Chloride) CONDUIT   19

Rigid Nonmetallic Conduit (PVC) is manufactured in three grades (Schedule 40, 80 and Type A) in trade sizes ½'' through 6''. Refer to charts in back of book for sizes available in each grade.

PVC is manufactured in standard 10' length including the coupling. For specific applications, it may be shipped in shorter or longer length, with or without couplings.

Article 347 of the National Electrical Code,® governs the use and installation of PVC.

Bending PVC

PVC is heated and then bent. This is done normally by two methods, HOTBOX® bending (electrical heating element) and Liquid submersion (propane gas heated).

HOTBOX® Bending: HOTBOX® benders come in different sizes to handle all sizes of PVC. Fig. 128a shows a HOTBOX® bender capable of heating PVC pipe up to 2'' trade size.

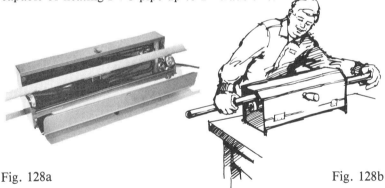

Fig. 128a   Fig. 128b

Courtesy — Thermotools Co.

The conduit is placed in the box and slowly rotated on the rollers so heat is evenly distributed (Fig. 128b). When the pipe becomes flexible, it is removed from the box, shaped to desired bend configuration and set by wiping with wet rags.

NOTE: The author has found that wearing standard household hot mits and dipping them in a bucket of cold water is easier and faster than using rags. The mits allow the hands to form around the conduit and cooling and setting of the hot conduit is quicker.

HOUSEHOLD HOT MIT

Bending PVC pipe 2'' trade size and larger with a HOTBOX® will require the use of an air tight plug in each end of the conduit (Fig. 129a). The plugs hold the hot expanding air inside the pipe. This heats the inside of the conduit and the expanded air makes bending possible without deforming or collapsing the pipe walls. The plugs must remain in place until the pipe is cooled and set. Fig. 129b shows a HOTBOX® bender capable of bending ½'' through 6'' PVC. This model is also available with Power Drive for automatic rotation of the pipe.

Fig. 129a   Courtesty — Thermotools Co.   Fig. 129b

NOTE: The plugs must remain in place until the pipe is cooled and set.

The PVC bender in Fig. 130a operates with propane gas that heats a liquid (Triethylene Glycol) that surrounds the pipe. The pipe is left in the heated liquid until pliable, removed, formed (Fig. 130b) and cooled to set (Fig. 130c).

Fig. 130a

Courtesy — Greenlee Tool, Co.

HEAT

Fig. 130b
Courtesy — Greenlee Tool, Co.

BEND

Fig. 130c
Courtesy — Greenlee Tool, Co.

COOL

Another method of bending PVC is by using electric BENDER BLANKETS as illustrated in Figs. 131a, b and c.

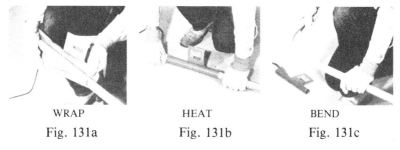

WRAP   HEAT   BEND

Fig. 131a   Fig. 131b   Fig. 131c

Courtesy — Enerpac, Co.

NOTE: Field bends can be made with some success using a torch. Care must be exercised as the PVC will take on a brownish color if flame is brought too close to the conduit. Scorched pipe may be rejected by some inspection authorities.

Finding An
Unknown Radius   **20**

The following procedure may be used to find the radius of large tanks, silos or curved roofs as shown in Fig. 132.

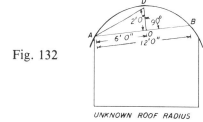

Fig. 132

A-B Cord of arc
O Center point cord of arc
O-D Height of arc
A-D Cord of half the arc

UNKNOWN ROOF RADIUS

Formula: Radius equals the cord of half the arc squared, divided by twice the height of the arc.

$$R = \frac{C^2}{2A}$$

R = Radius   C = Cord of half the arc   A = Height of arc

The cord of the arc is found by laying out two points on the circle, A and B, (the points must be less than the diameter) and measuring between these points (Fig. 132). For ease of figuring, these points can be set at even spacing, i.e. 8', 10', etc. This makes locating the center of the cord easier and facilitates finding the height of the arc.

The height of the arc is found by measuring at a right angle from the center of the cord of the arc to the outside of the circle. Line O-D of Fig. 132.

Cord of half the arc is the measurement from Point A to Point D or the hypotenuse (Fig. 132). Using Pythagorean's Theorem (as discussed in Chapter 1) we can find the hypotenuse or cord of half the arc.

Using Pythagorean's Theorem

$$H = \sqrt{A^2 + 0^2}$$

H = Hypotenuse or cord of half the arc (A-D)
A = Adjacent side (A-O)
O = Opposite side (O-D)

Substitute and solve

$H = \sqrt{6^2 + 2^2}$ $H = \sqrt{36 + 4}$ $H = \sqrt{40}$

$H = 6.32$

Cord of half the arc $= 6.32'$

Using the formula

$R = \dfrac{C^2}{2A}$

Substitute and solve

$R = \dfrac{(6.32)^2}{2 \times 2}$ $R = \dfrac{39.94}{4}$ $R = 9.98'$

Radius $= 9'\ 11\frac{3}{4}''$

If the cord of half the arc can be measured as shown in Fig. 133, the radius can be determined without using Pythagorean's Theorem and applying the values directly to the formula:

$R = \dfrac{C^2}{2A}$

R = Radius
C = Cord of half the arc
A = Height of arc

Substitute values and solve

$R = \dfrac{(39.5)^2}{2 \times 16.25}$ $R = \dfrac{1560.25}{32.5}$ $R = 48.00$

Radius $= 48''$

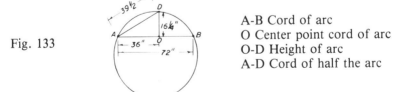

Fig. 133

A-B Cord of arc
O Center point cord of arc
O-D Height of arc
A-D Cord of half the arc

The radius can be found of an existing pipe as shown in Fig. 134 by using the same procedure as outlined for the curved roof (Fig. 132) or the silo (Fig. 133).

97

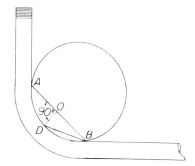

Fig. 134

PROBLEM:

1. Find the radius of an existing pipe if the cord of arc is 20'' and the height of the arc is 3''.

2. Find the radius of a silo with the following dimensions: Cord of the arc is 41'0'', height of arc is 5'4''. **Hint:** Convert feet to inches.

Another method for determining an unknown radius, is to establish two cord of arc lines and locate the center of each cord. Lines are then established at right angles from the center of each cord. The intersection of these lines is the center of the circle. The radius may be found by measuring from this point to the outside of the circle. (Fig. 135)

Fig. 135

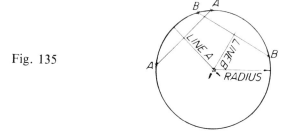

An alternate and purely trial and error method to determine the radius of an existing bend, requires only a string and piece of chalk, or other suitable marking device. The chalk is attached to the string and a pivot point is found that will duplicate the shape of the bend. When this point is located a complete circle is drawn. The radius can now be found by measuring from the pivot point to the outside of the circle. (Fig. 136).

98

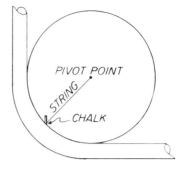

Fig. 136

BENDING PIPE WITH LARGER THAN NORMAL RADIUS

Once the radius has been determined as outlined in the previous chapter or obtained from the job plans or prints, the layout for bending pipe that must conform to the walls of large grain silos, circular storage tanks, etc. is basically a segment layout calculated from radius expressed in feet.

Fig. 137 might be typical of a larger than normal radius bending job. The figure shows a storage tank 18' in diameter with a rigid pipe run between two junction boxes.

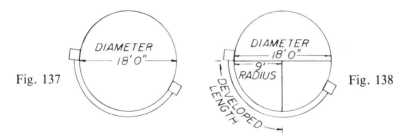

Fig. 137   Fig. 138

If the diameter of the tank is 18 feet, then the radius is 9 feet (Fig. 138) and this radius (9') will be used for calculating the spacing between the bend marks for segment bending the conduit.

Regardless of the actual distance between the boxes, we must first calculate the developed length for a radius of 9' to determine spacing between the bend marks. This spacing will then be typical for the entire length of the conduit run.

NOTE: The formulas for segment layout are covered in detail in Chapter 15

To find the developed length or the amount of pipe that will be required to bend a given radius.

Developed Length = 1.57 X Radius

NOTE: Convert any radius in feet to radius in inches. 9 (feet) X 12 (inches) = 108''

D.L. = 1.57 X 108''
D.L. = 169.56''

The developed length of 169.56'' is the amount of conduit that will be required to bend a pipe with a 108'' (9 foot) radius.

The developed length can now be divided into segments for bending. Remembering from our previous discussion on segment bending, that the smaller the degree of bend, the smoother the radius will be. This is especially important with larger than normal radius bending if the finished pipe is to look right and conform well to the tank wall.

Bending 5° per segment (shot) will give us the smooth appearance we want. The radius of 108'' (9') with a developed length of 169.56'' will require 18 shots (90° divided by 5).

By dividing developed length (169.56'') by number of shots (18), we get the spacing between the shots.

$$\frac{\text{Developed Length}}{\text{Shots}} \quad \frac{169.56}{18} = 9.42 \text{ or approximately } 9\ 3/8''$$

Referring back to Fig. 138, it is important to remember that the developed length only makes up one quarter (¼) of the circumference of the storage tank. The actual pipe between the junction boxes will require more than 169.56'' because the distance between the boxes is greater than ¼ of the circumference of the tank. The actual distance can be measured to determine total pipe required, but the spacing between bend marks and degree of bend will be the same for the entire length of the pipe.

For this problem we will assume the actual measurement between the boxes is 38' 9 7/8'' or 465 7/8''. By dividing this figure 465 7/8'' by 120'' (nominal length for rigid conduit including the coupling) we get 3.88. this job then will take almost 4 sticks of rigid conduit.

The only thing left to consider before starting the layout is the couplings that will be required to connect the pieces of pipe together. We cannot bend on the couplings, so the layout must be adjusted accordingly. With 9 3/8'' spacing between the bend marks, that means that at each coupling, the marks should be placed 4 23/32'' or approx. 4¾'' either side of center of the coupling. This will probably require that one or more of the pipes be cut and rethreaded to make the layout come out right. If the layout, however, comes within an 1'' or 1½'' of the desired measurement at the coupling, the marks can be adjusted to approximately the desired spacing without adversely effecting the total pipe job and thus eliminate the need for cutting and threading (Fig. 139).

Fig. 139

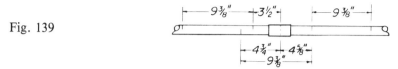

This first pipe should also be laid out with the first mark 4¾'' (approx. half of 9 3/8'') from the end of the conduit and the remaining marks placed 9 3/8'' apart. This will give the conduit run the same smooth appearance from the junction box and at each coupling (Fig. 140).

Fig. 140

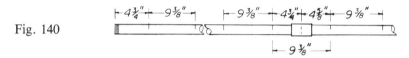

To make the bends at the first few bend marks when using a hydraulic bender, screw a short piece of pipe on the end of the conduit to be bent so the pipe can be supported on the pivot shoe (Fig. 141).

Fig. 141

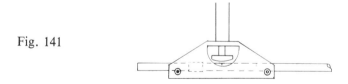

This method can also be used when short stubs are required for regular radius segment bending.

NOTE: Be sure coupling and short piece of pipe are made up wrench tight when employing this technique to prevent damage to the threads.

When bending larger than normal radius pipe with a "CHICAGO", the pipe will have to be removed from the bender and reversed for the last few bends.

Bending pipe with larger than normal radius using a bending table and bending degree protractor.

Bending larger than normal radius using the "Amount of Travel Method."

VALUES OF THE TRIGONOMETRIC FUNCTIONS

ANGLE	SINE	COSINE	TANGENT	COTANGENT	COSECANT
1°	.0175	.9998	.0175	57.3	57.3065
2°	.0349	.9994	.0349	28.6	28.6532
3°	.0523	.9986	.0524	19.1	19.1058
4°	.0698	.9976	.0699	14.3	14.3348
5°	.0872	.9962	.0875	11.4	11.4731
6°	.1045	.9945	.1051	9.51	9.5666
7°	.1219	.9925	.1228	8.14	8.2054
8°	.1392	.9903	.1405	7.12	7.1854
9°	.1564	.9877	.1584	6.31	6.3926
10°	.1736	.9848	.1763	5.67	5.7587
11°	.1908	.9816	.1944	5.14	5.2408
12°	.2079	.9781	.2126	4.70	4.8097
13°	.2250	.9744	.2309	4.33	4.4454
14°	.2419	.9703	.2493	4.01	4.1335
15°	.2588	.9659	.2679	3.73	3.8636
16°	.2756	.9613	.2867	3.49	3.5915
17°	.2924	.9563	.3057	3.27	3.4203
18°	.3090	.9511	.3249	3.08	3.2360
19°	.3256	.9455	.3443	2.90	3.0715
20°	.3420	.9397	.3640	2.75	2.9238
21°	.3584	.9336	.3839	2.61	2.7904
22°	.3746	.9272	.4040	2.48	2.6694
23°	.3907	.9205	.4245	2.36	2.5593
24°	.4067	.9135	.4452	2.25	2.4585
25°	.4226	.9063	.4663	2.14	2.3661
26°	.4384	.8988	.4877	2.05	2.2811
27°	.4540	.8910	.5095	1.96	2.2026
28°	.4695	.8829	.5317	1.88	2.1300
29°	.4848	.8746	.5543	1.80	2.0626
30°	.5000	.8660	.5774	1.73	2.0000
31°	.5150	.8572	.6009	1.66	1.9415
32°	.5299	.8480	.6249	1.60	1.8870
33°	.5446	.8387	.6494	1.54	1.8360
34°	.5592	.8290	.6745	1.48	1.7883
35°	.5736	.8192	.7002	1.43	1.7434
36°	.5878	.8090	.7265	1.38	1.7012
37°	.6018	.7986	.7536	1.33	1.6616
38°	.6157	.7880	.7813	1.28	1.6242
39°	.6293	.7771	.8098	1.23	1.5890
40°	.6428	.7660	.8391	1.19	1.5557
41°	.6561	.7547	.8693	1.15	1.5242
42°	.6691	.7431	.9004	1.11	1.4944
43°	.6820	.7314	.9325	1.07	1.4662
44°	.6947	.7193	.9657	1.04	1.4395
45°	.7071	.7071	1.0000	1.00	1.4142
46°	.7193	.6947	1.0355	.966	1.4395
47°	.7314	.6820	1.0724	.933	1.3673
48°	.7431	.6691	1.1106	.900	1.3456
49°	.7547	.6561	1.1504	.869	1.3250
50°	.7660	.6428	1.1918	.839	1.3054
51°	.7771	.6293	1.2349	.810	1.2867
52°	.7880	.6157	1.2799	.781	1.2690
53°	.7986	.6018	1.3270	.754	1.2521
54°	.8090	.5878	1.3764	.727	1.2360
55°	.8192	.5736	1.4281	.700	1.2207
56°	.8290	.5592	1.4826	.675	1.2062
57°	.8387	.5446	1.5399	.649	1.1923
58°	.8480	.5299	1.6003	.625	1.1791
59°	.8572	.5150	1.6643	.601	1.1666
60°	.8660	.5000	1.7321	.577	1.1547
61°	.8746	.4848	1.8040	.554	1.1433
62°	.8829	.4695	1.8807	.532	1.1325
63°	.8910	.4540	1.9626	.510	1.1223
64°	.8988	.4384	2.0503	.488	1.1126
65°	.9063	.4226	2.1445	.466	1.1033
66°	.9135	.4067	2.2460	.445	1.0946
67°	.9205	.3907	2.3559	.424	1.0863
68°	.9272	.3746	2.4751	.404	1.0785
69°	.9336	.3584	2.6051	.384	1.0711
70°	.9397	.3420	2.7475	.364	1.0641
71°	.9455	.3256	2.9042	.344	1.0576
72°	.9511	.3090	3.0777	.325	1.0514
73°	.9563	.2924	3.2709	.306	1.0456
74°	.9613	.2756	3.4874	.287	1.0402
75°	.9659	.2588	3.7321	.268	1.0352
76°	.9703	.2419	4.0108	.249	1.0306
77°	.9744	.2250	4.3315	.231	1.0263
78°	.9781	.2079	4.7046	.213	1.0223
79°	.9816	.1908	5.1446	.194	1.0187
80°	.9848	.1736	5.6713	.176	1.0154
81°	.9877	.1564	6.3138	.158	1.0124
82°	.9903	.1392	7.1154	.141	1.0098
83°	.9925	.1219	8.1443	.123	1.0075
84°	.9945	.1045	9.5144	.105	1.0055
85°	.9962	.0872	11.4300	.088	1.0038
86°	.9976	.0698	14.3010	.070	1.0024
87°	.9986	.0523	19.0810	.052	1.0013
88°	.9994	.0349	28.6360	.035	1.0006
89°	.9998	.0175	57.2900	.018	1.0001
90°	1.0000	.0000	∞	.000	1.0000

Both the Trig chart and the fraction equivalents for decimals on a wallet sized cut-out card are located on the last page of this book.

DECIMAL AND METRIC EQUIVALENT OF COMMON FRACTIONS OF AN INCH

FRACTION	DECIMAL	Mm
1/32	.03125	.794
1/16	.06250	1.588
3/32	.09375	2.381
1/8	.12500	3.175
5/32	.15625	3.969
3/16	.18750	4.763
7/32	.21875	5.556
1/4	.25000	6.350
9/32	.28125	7.144
5/16	.31250	7.938
11/32	.34375	8.731
3/8	.37500	9.525
13/32	.40625	10.319
7/16	.43750	11.113
15/32	.46875	11.906
1/2	.50000	12.700
17/32	.53125	13.494
9/16	.56250	14.288
19/32	.59375	15.081
5/8	.62500	15.875
21/32	.65625	16.669
11/16	.68750	17.463
23/32	.71875	18.256
3/4	.75000	19.050
25/32	.78125	19.844
13/16	.81250	20.638
27/32	.84375	21.431
7/8	.87500	22.225
29/32	.90625	23.019
15/16	.93750	23.813
31/32	.96875	24.606
1/1	1.00000	25.400

EMT

TRADE SIZE	OUTSIDE DIAMETER	INSIDE DIAMETER	WALL THICKNESS	WEIGHT PER 100'	FT. PER BUNDLE
1/2	0.706	0.622	.042	30	100
3/4	0.922	0.824	.049	45	100
1	1.163	1.049	.057	65	100
1 1/4	1.510	1.380	.065	96	50
1 1/2	1.740	1.610	.065	111	50
2	2.197	2.067	.065	141	30
2 1/2	2.875	2.731	.072	230	10
3	3.500	3.356	.072	270	10
4	4.500	4.334	.083	400	10

RIGID STEEL

TRADE SIZE	OUTSIDE DIAMETER	INSIDE DIAMETER	WALL THICKNESS	WEIGHT PER 100'	FT. PER BUNDLE
1/2	0.840	0.622	.109	80	100
3/4	1.050	0.824	.113	106	50
1	1.315	1.049	.133	153	50
1 1/4	1.660	1.380	.140	201	30
1 1/2	1.900	1.610	.145	249	30
2	2.375	2.067	.154	334	10
2 1/2	2.875	2.469	.203	527	10
3	3.500	3.068	.216	690	10
3 1/2	4.000	3.548	.226	831	10
4	4.500	4.026	.237	982	10
5	5.563	5.047	.258	1344	10
6	6.625	6.065	.280	1770	10

RIGID ALUMINUM

TRADE SIZE	OUTSIDE DIAMETER	INSIDE DIAMETER	WALL THICKNESS	WEIGHT PER 100'	FT. PER BUNDLE
1/2	0.840	0.622	.109	30	100
3/4	1.050	0.824	.113	37	100
1	1.315	1.049	.133	60	100
1 1/4	1.660	1.380	.140	78	100
1 1/2	1.900	1.610	.145	100	50
2	2.375	2.067	.154	125	30
2 1/2	2.875	2.469	.203	200	10
3	3.500	3.068	.216	260	10
3 1/2	4.000	3.548	.226	330	10
4	4.500	4.026	.237	370	10
5	5.563	5.047	.258	530	10
6	6.625	6.065	.280	660	10

IMC

TRADE SIZE	OUTSIDE DIAMETER	INSIDE DIAMETER	WALL THICKNESS	WEIGHT PER 100'	FT. PER BUNDLE
1/2	0.815	0.675	.070	58	100
3/4	1.029	0.879	.075	79	100
1	1.290	1.120	.085	114	50
1 1/4	1.638	1.468	.090	146	30
1 1/2	1.883	1.703	.095	179	30
2	2.360	2.170	.130	239	10
2 1/2	2.857	2.597	.130	402	10
3	3.476	3.216	.130	495	10
3 1/2	3.971	3.711	.130	576	10
4	4.466	4.206	.130	642	10

PVC TYPE A

TRADE SIZE	OUTSIDE DIAMETER	INSIDE DIAMETER	WALL THICKNESS	WEIGHT PER 100'	FT. PER BUNDLE
1/2	0.840	0.720	.060	11	100
3/4	1.050	0.930	.060	13	100
1	1.315	1.195	.060	17	100
1 1/4	1.660	1.520	.070	25	50
1 1/2	1.900	1.740	.080	32	50
2	2.375	2.175	.100	50	10
2 1/2	2.875	2.655	.110	67	10
3	3.500	3.250	.125	90	10
4	4.500	4.200	.150	146	10

106

PVC TYPE 40 (Schedule 40)

TRADE SIZE	OUTSIDE DIAMETER	INSIDE DIAMETER	WALL THICKNESS	WEIGHT PER 100'	FT. PER BUNDLE
1/2	0.840	0.622	.109	16	100
3/4	1.050	0.824	.113	22	100
1	1.315	1.049	.133	32	100
1 1/4	1.660	1.380	.140	43	50
1 1/2	1.900	1.610	.145	52	50
2	2.375	2.067	.154	69	10
2 1/2	2.875	2.469	.203	109	10
3	3.500	3.068	.216	142	10
3 1/2	4.000	3.548	.226	170	10
4	4.500	4.026	.237	202	10
5	5.563	5.047	.258	271	10
6	6.625	6.065	.280	350	10

PVC TYPE 80 (Schedule 80)

TRADE SIZE	OUTSIDE DIAMETER	INSIDE DIAMETER	WALL THICKNESS	WEIGHT PER 100'	FT. PER BUNDLE
1/2	0.840	0.546	.147	21	100
3/4	1.050	0.742	.154	28	100
1	1.315	0.957	.179	41	100
1 1/4	1.660	1.278	.191	57	50
1 1/2	1.900	1.500	.200	68	50
2	2.375	1.939	.218	94	10
2 1/2	2.857	2.323	.276	142	10
3	3.500	2.900	.300	190	10
3 1/2	4.000	3.364	.318	232	10
4	4.500	3.826	.337	278	10
5	5.563	4.813	.375	385	10
6	6.625	5.761	.432	530	10

CONDUIT SPACING CHART

This chart gives center to center measurements for conduit layout. Locate the smallest conduit across the bottom line and then locate the larger conduit on the vertical line. The figure given is the center-to-center measurement of the conduits. To this value add the desired spacing between conduits.

Example: Layout a 2½" and 3½" conduit with 2" spacing. The center-to-center measurement is 3.438", add 2" for spacing. 3.438" + 2" = 5.438 or approximately 5 7/16" center-to-center for layout. This layout can be used for punching knock-outs · or any other layout figured on center-to-center measurement.

L A R G E S T

LARGEST	1/2	3/4	1	1 1/4	1 1/2	2	2 1/2	3	3 1/2	4	5	6
1/2	0.840											
3/4	0.945	1.050										
1	1.078	1.183	1.315									
1 1/4	1.250	1.355	1.488	1.660								
1 1/2	1.370	1.475	1.608	1.780	1.900							
2	1.608	1.713	1.846	2.018	2.138	2.375						
2 1/2	1.858	1.963	2.096	2.268	2.388	2.626	2.876					
3	2.170	2.275	2.408	2.580	2.700	2.938	3.188	3.500				
3 1/2	2.420	2.525	2.658	2.830	2.950	3.188	3.438	3.750	4.000			
4	2.670	2.775	2.908	3.080	3.200	3.438	3.688	4.000	4.250	4.500		
5	3.202	3.307	3.440	3.612	3.732	3.970	4.220	4.532	4.782	5.032	5.564	
6	3.733	3.838	3.971	4.143	4.263	4.501	4.751	5.063	5.313	5.563	6.095	6.626
	1/2	3/4	1	1 1/4	1 1/2	2	2 1/2	3	3 1/2	4	5	6

SMALLEST

IMC BENDING EQUIPMENT

HAND BENDERS	1/2	3/4	1	1 1/4	1 1/2	2	2 1/2	3	3 1/2	4
Enerpac	B-7	B-10								
Gardner	940	941								
Greenlee	841	842	843							

MECHANICAL BENDERS	1/2	3/4	1	1 1/4	1 1/2	2	2 1/2	3	3 1/2	4
Enerpac Side Winder	X	X	X							
Greenlee 1800	X	X	X							
Greenlee 1818R	X	X	X							
Lidseen 5100	X	X	X							
Lidseen 5200					X	X				

ELECTRIC BENDERS	1/2	3/4	1	1 1/4	1 1/2	2	2 1/2	3	3 1/2	4
Enerpac Cyclone	X	X	X	X	X	X				
Greenlee 555 I					X	X				

HYDRAULIC BENDERS	1/2	3/4	1	1 1/4	1 1/2	2	2 1/2	3	3 1/2	4
Enerpac Mini Eegor			X	X	X	X				
Enerpac Eegor							X	X	X	X
Greenlee 882CB					X	X	X			
Greenlee 881/B with attachments					X	X	X	X	X	X

MISCELLANEOUS ELECTRICAL FORMULAS

OHMS LAW:

To find the current in amperes (amps):

$$\text{Amps} = \frac{\text{Volts}}{\text{Ohms}} \quad \text{or} \quad I = \frac{E}{R}$$

To find the Voltage (volts):

Volts = Amps X Ohms or E = I X R

To find the resistance in ohms:

$$\text{Ohms} = \frac{\text{Volts}}{\text{Amps}} \quad \text{or} \quad R = \frac{E}{I}$$

POWER FORMULAS

One horsepower = 746 watts   One kilowatt = 1000 watts

DIRECT-CURRENT CIRCUITS

Power in Watts = Volts X Amps

To find current in amperes (amps):

$$\text{Amps} = \frac{\text{Watts}}{\text{Volts}} \quad \text{or} \quad I = \frac{W}{E}$$

$$\frac{\text{Current}}{\text{(of a motor)}} = \frac{\text{Horsepower X 746}}{\text{Volts X Efficiency}} \quad \text{or} \quad I = \frac{\text{hp. X 746}}{\text{E X Eff.}}$$

To find the voltage (volts:)

$$\text{Volts} = \frac{\text{Watts}}{\text{Amps}} \quad \text{or} \quad E = \frac{W}{I}$$

SINGLE PHASE CIRCUITS

Power in Watts = Volts X Amperes X Power Factor

To find current in amperes:

$$\text{Amps} = \frac{\text{Watts}}{\text{Volts X Power Factor}} \quad \text{or} \quad I = \frac{W}{\text{E X P.F.}}$$

$$\frac{\text{Current}}{\text{(of a motor)}} = \frac{\text{Horsepower X 746}}{\text{Volts X Power Factor X Efficiency}}$$

$$\text{or} \quad I = \frac{\text{hp. X 746}}{\text{E X P.F. X Eff.}}$$

TWO-PHASE ALTERNATING-CURRENT CIRCUITS

Power in Watts = Volts X Amperes X Power Factor X 2

To find current in amperes in each wire:

$$\text{Amps} = \frac{\text{Watts}}{\text{Volts X Power Factor X 2}}$$

$$\frac{\text{Current}}{\text{(of a motor)}} = \frac{\text{Horsepower X 746}}{\text{Volts X Power Factor X Efficiency X 2}}$$

THREE-PHASE ALTERNATING-CURRENT CIRCUITS

Power in Watts = Volts X Amperes X Power Factor X 1.73

To find current in amperes in each wire:

$$\text{Amps} = \frac{\text{Watts}}{\text{Volts X Power Factor X 1.73}}$$

$$\frac{\text{Current}}{\text{(of a motor)}} = \frac{\text{Horsepower X 746}}{\text{Volts X Power Factor X Efficiency X 1.73}}$$

VOLTAGE DROP
DIRECT CURRENT AND SINGLE & TWO PHASE CIRCUITS

To find size of conductor required:

$$\text{Cm} = \frac{21.6 \text{ X I X D}}{\text{Vd}}$$

Cm = Wire Size in Circular Mils
I = Load Current in Amps
D = Distance To Load (1 Way)
Vd = Allowable Voltage Drop (3 to 5%)
21.6 = Constant for Copper Wire
       (Use 34 for Aluminum Wire).

To find voltage drop in circuit:

$$\text{Vd} = \frac{21.6 \text{ X I X D}}{\text{Cm}}$$

To find allowable one way distance for a given voltage drop:

$$\text{D} = \frac{\text{Cm X Vd}}{21.6 \text{ X I}}$$

THREE PHASE CIRCUITS

To find size of conductors required:

$$\text{Cm} = \frac{18.7 \text{ X I X D}}{\text{Vd}}$$

Cm = Wire Size in Circular Mils
I = Load Current in Amps
D = Distance To Load (1 Way)
Vd = Allowable Voltage Drop (3 to 5%)
18.7 = Constant for Copper Wire
(Use 29.4 for Aluminum Wire).

To find voltage drop in a circuit:

$$Vd = \frac{18.7 \times I \times D}{Cm}$$

To find allowable one-way distance for a given voltage drop:

$$D = \frac{Cm \times Vd}{18.7 \times I}$$

GLOSSARY

Arc: Any part of the circumference of a circle.

Back-To-Back: Two ninety degree bends in one conduit, usually with both stubs turned up on the same plane forming a "U".

BENDERS:

"**CHICAGO**": A general term applied to all hand ratcheted, frame mounted, benders. (The name is actually the trade name of the Lidseen Co. of North Carolina, who produced one of the first benders of this type, for this reason the word Chicago will be capitalized and set in quotations when used in the text.) See Figs. 75 and 76

Hand Benders — Benders having a full shoe that the pipe is formed around. Used for hand bending EMT, IMC and Rigid Pipe.

Hickey — A hand held bender with no bending shoe, used to bend rigid conduit. Used where accuracy or duplication is not essential. See Fig. 73a

Hot Box — A broad term used to describe heat devices used to soften PVC pipe for bending.

Hydraulic — A bender consisting of a hydraulic pump (hand or electric), ram assembly, frame, bending shoe (one-shot or segment), bending supports and pins. Used for bending larger conduit. See Fig. 71, 72 and 100

BENDING SHOE:

One-Shot — A full 90° radius shoe used with hydraulic benders. See Fig. 103

Segment — A bending shoe with a radius less than 90°. See Fig. 104

Bending Table: A table used for hydraulic benders. It has a movable pipe vise for securing the conduit, and bender supports. See Fig. 117

Bite: Placing the bender or hickey on the conduit and pulling an amount of bend less than 90°. See Fig. 74

Circumference: The distance around a circle.

Concentric Bends: Pipe having a common center with increasing or decreasing radii. This method of bending is employed when even spacing is required for the full length on the bend. See Fig. 123

Cord of Arc: A straight line joining the ends of an arc. A distance less than the diameter.

Cord of Half the Arc: The length of a line if it was placed diagonally from the edge of the cord of arc to the high point of the arc.

Degrees Per Shot: The amount of bend in degrees a pipe is to be bent for each bend mark of a segment bend.

Developed Length: The amount of straight pipe needed to bend a given radius.

Diameter: The distance across the center of a circle.

Dog-Leg: An unwanted alignment between bends of an offset that makes the pipe look like a dog's hind leg.

Ductility: Ability of a material to be shaped or formed.

Gain: The amount of pipe gained (saved) by bending on a radius and not at right angles.

Hickey: See benders.

Kick: A bend of less than 90° placed in a conduit to change direction. See Fig. 25

Leg Length: The length of pipe measured from the back of the bend.

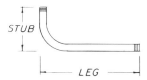

Ninety Degree Bend: Any radius bend in a conduit that changes the direction of the pipe 90°.

Number of Bending Shots: The number depends on the size of the radius and the smoothness required of the bend.

O.D. Size: Outside diameter of a pipe.

Offset: Two identical bends placed in a conduit to change direction or elevation of the pipe run.

Oh-Oh: A pipe bent wrong that can't be used. Usually thrown out or said to be put in the oh-oh pile.

Pivot Shoes (Pipe Supports): Castings formed to the shape of each conduit size and held in the bender frame by pins.

Plunger (Ram): The rod in the hydraulic cylinder which is attached to the bending shoe and moves forward when hydraulic pressure is applied.

Radius: The relative size of the bent portion of a pipe.

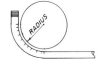

112

Reference Point: A mark used to locate the edge of an obstruction for bending saddles.

Segment Bend: Any bend formed by a series of bends of a few degrees each, rather than a single one-shot bend.

Shot: One bend in a segment bend.

Shrink: The amount a conduit reduces in total length after an offset is bent.

Spring Back: The amount a bent pipe tends to straighten after the bending force is removed.

Stub: The distance from the back of the bend to the end of the conduit.

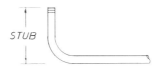

Sweep: A 90° bend with a radius larger than the standard one-shot shoe.

Take-Up (Come-back): The amount that must be subtracted from the desired stub length to make the bend come out right using a point of reference on the bender or bending shoe.

WOW (Hoop-de-do): An improperly made bend where the conduit was not held secure and bend is not true or aligned right. The term is also used to indicate a slight bend made by hand or over the knee for correction or direction change.

ANSWERS TO PROBLEMS

Page 7

1. $O = S \times H$ $.5 \times 48 = 24''$

   $24'' \div 48'' = .5''$ $.5 \times 12''$ or $6''$ rise/ft.

2. $T = \dfrac{O}{A} = \dfrac{10}{14.5} = .6896$ or $35°$

3. $C = \dfrac{A}{H} = \dfrac{40}{100} = .4$ or $66°$

   $O = S \times H$ $.9135 \times 100 =$
   91.35 or $91'4\text{-}3/16''$

4. $T = \dfrac{O}{A} = \dfrac{7}{3} = 2.337$ or $67°$

All answers rounded to nearest 1/8".

Page 22

1. (a) 31"   (b) 44"   (c) 85"

Page 25

1.

2.

3.

4.

5.

Page 33

1.

2.

Page 40 - Method #1

1.

2.

Page 41 - Method #2

1.

2.

Page 45

Multiplier of 2.5

1.

2.

Multiplier of 3

3.

4.

Page 57

1.   (a) 1-25/32''   (b) 3-17/32''

2.   (a) 5-29/32''   (b) 4-7/16''

Page 61

1. 76¼''   2. 77½''   3. 73-3/8''   4. 86½''

115

Page 67

1.

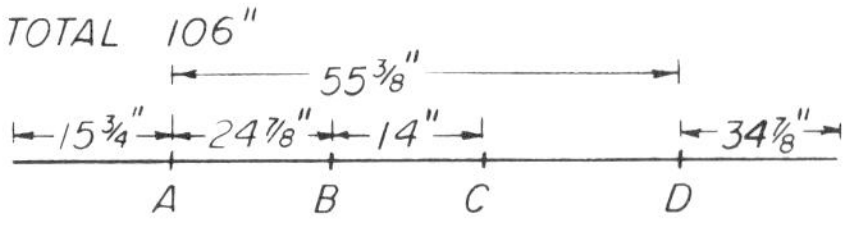
TOTAL 106"
55⅜"
15¾"
24⅞"
14"
34⅞"
A
B
C
D

2.

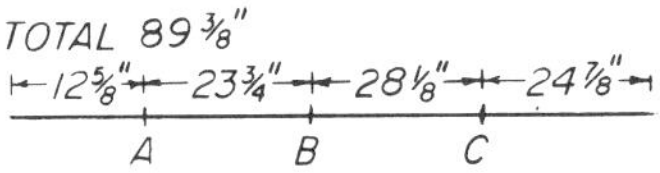
TOTAL 89⅜"
12⅝"
23¾"
28⅛"
24⅞"
A
B
C

3.

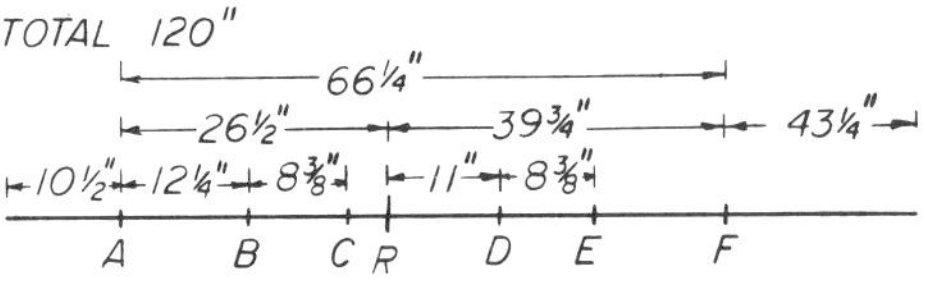
TOTAL 120"
66¼"
26½"
39¾"
43¼"
10½"
12¼"
8⅜"
11"
8⅜"
A
B
C
R
D
E
F

Page 78

1. Start Mark 35-1/8" Spacing 1-7/8"

2. Start Mark 23-½" Spacing 2-1/8"

Page 89

First Pipe	Developed Length 28.26" ÷ 20 Spacing 1-3/8" Start Mark 27-5/8"
Second Pipe	Radius 22.375" Developed Length 35.128" ÷ 20 Spacing 1¾" Start Mark 27-5/8"
Third Pipe	Radius 28.375" Developed Length 44.548" ÷ 20 Spacing 2¼" Start Mark 27-5/8"

Page 98

1.

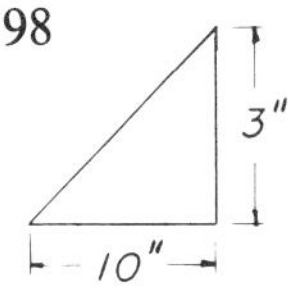
3"
10"

$$H = \sqrt{10^2 + 3^2} = 10.440$$

$$R = \frac{C^2}{2A} = \frac{10.44^2}{2 \times 3} = 18.16 \text{ or } 18\text{-}1/8''$$

2.

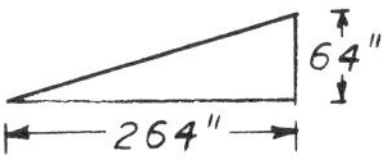
64"
264"

$$H. = \sqrt{20.5^2 + 5.3^2} = 21.174$$

$$R = \frac{C^2}{2A} = \frac{254.188^2}{2 \times 64} = \frac{64612}{128} = 504.78'' \text{ or } 42'\tfrac{3}{4}''$$

ANGLE	SINE	COSINE	TANGENT	COTANGENT	COSECANT
1°	.0175	.9998	.0175	57.3	57.3065
2°	.0349	.9994	.0349	28.6	28.6532
3°	.0523	.9986	.0524	19.1	19.1058
4°	.0698	.9976	.0699	14.3	14.3348
5°	.0872	.9962	.0875	11.4	11.4731
6°	.1045	.9945	.1051	9.51	9.5666
7°	.1219	.9925	.1228	8.14	8.2054
8°	.1392	.9903	.1405	7.12	7.1854
9°	.1564	.9877	.1584	6.31	6.3926
10°	.1736	.9848	.1763	5.67	5.7587
11°	.1908	.9816	.1944	5.14	5.2408
12°	.2079	.9781	.2126	4.70	4.8097
13°	.2250	.9744	.2309	4.33	4.4454
14°	.2419	.9703	.2493	4.01	4.1335
15°	.2588	.9659	.2679	3.73	3.8636
16°	.2756	.9613	.2867	3.49	3.6279
17°	.2924	.9563	.3057	3.27	3.4203
18°	.3090	.9511	.3249	3.08	3.2360
19°	.3256	.9455	.3443	2.90	3.0715
20°	.3420	.9397	.3640	2.75	2.9238
21°	.3584	.9336	.3839	2.61	2.7904
22°	.3746	.9272	.4040	2.48	2.6694
23°	.3907	.9205	.4245	2.36	2.5593
24°	.4067	.9135	.4452	2.25	2.4585
25°	.4226	.9063	.4663	2.14	2.3661
26°	.4384	.8988	.4877	2.05	2.2811
27°	.4540	.8910	.5095	1.96	2.2026
28°	.4695	.8829	.5317	1.88	2.1300
29°	.4848	.8746	.5543	1.80	2.0626
30°	.5000	.8660	.5774	1.73	2.0000
31°	.5150	.8572	.6009	1.66	1.9415
32°	.5299	.8480	.6249	1.60	1.8870
33°	.5446	.8387	.6494	1.54	1.8360
34°	.5592	.8290	.6745	1.48	1.7883
35°	.5736	.8192	.7002	1.43	1.7434
36°	.5878	.8090	.7265	1.38	1.7012
37°	.6018	.7986	.7536	1.33	1.6616
38°	.6157	.7880	.7813	1.28	1.6242
39°	.6293	.7771	.8098	1.23	1.5890
40°	.6428	.7660	.8391	1.19	1.5557
41°	.6561	.7547	.8693	1.15	1.5242
42°	.6691	.7431	.9004	1.11	1.4944
43°	.6820	.7314	.9325	1.07	1.4662
44°	.6947	.7193	.9657	1.04	1.4395
45°	.7071	.7071	1.0000	1.00	1.4142

FRACTION	DECIMAL
1/32	.03125
1/16	.06250
3/32	.09375
1/8	.12500
5/32	.15625
3/16	.18750
7/32	.21875
1/4	.25000
9/32	.28125
5/16	.31250
11/32	.34375
3/8	.37500
13/32	.40625
7/16	.43750
15/32	.46875
1/2	.50000
17/32	.53125
9/16	.56250
19/32	.59375
5/8	.62500
21/32	.65625
11/16	.68750
23/32	.71875
3/4	.75000
25/32	.78125
13/16	.81250
27/32	.84375
7/8	.87500
29/32	.90625
15/16	.93750
31/32	.96875
1/1	1.00000

ANGLE	SINE	COSINE	TANGENT	COTANGENT	COSECANT
46°	.7193	.6947	1.0355	.966	1.3902
47°	.7314	.6820	1.0724	.933	1.3673
48°	.7431	.6691	1.1106	.900	1.3456
49°	.7547	.6561	1.1504	.869	1.3250
50°	.7660	.6428	1.1918	.839	1.3054
51°	.7771	.6293	1.2349	.810	1.2867
52°	.7880	.6157	1.2799	.781	1.2690
53°	.7986	.6018	1.3270	.754	1.2521
54°	.8090	.5878	1.3764	.727	1.2361
55°	.8192	.5736	1.4281	.700	1.2207
56°	.8290	.5592	1.4826	.675	1.2062
57°	.8387	.5446	1.5399	.649	1.1923
58°	.8480	.5299	1.6003	.625	1.1791
59°	.8572	.5150	1.6643	.601	1.1666
60°	.8660	.5000	1.7321	.577	1.1547
61°	.8746	.4848	1.8040	.554	1.1433
62°	.8829	.4695	1.8807	.532	1.1325
63°	.8910	.4540	1.9626	.510	1.1223
64°	.8988	.4384	2.0503	.488	1.1126
65°	.9063	.4226	2.1445	.466	1.1033
66°	.9135	.4067	2.2460	.445	1.0946
67°	.9205	.3907	2.3559	.424	1.0863
68°	.9272	.3746	2.4751	.404	1.0785
69°	.9336	.3584	2.6051	.384	1.0711
70°	.9397	.3420	2.7475	.364	1.0641
71°	.9455	.3256	2.9042	.344	1.0576
72°	.9511	.3090	3.0777	.325	1.0514
73°	.9563	.2924	3.2709	.306	1.0456
74°	.9613	.2756	3.4874	.287	1.0402
75°	.9659	.2588	3.7321	.268	1.0352
76°	.9703	.2419	4.0108	.249	1.0306
77°	.9744	.2250	4.3315	.231	1.0263
78°	.9781	.2079	4.7046	.213	1.0223
79°	.9816	.1908	5.1446	.194	1.0187
80°	.9848	.1736	5.6713	.176	1.0154
81°	.9877	.1564	6.3138	.158	1.0125
82°	.9903	.1392	7.1154	.141	1.0098
83°	.9925	.1219	8.1443	.123	1.0075
84°	.9945	.1045	9.5144	.105	1.0055
85°	.9962	.0872	11.4300	.088	1.0038
86°	.9976	.0698	14.3010	.070	1.0024
87°	.9986	.0523	19.0810	.052	1.0013
88°	.9994	.0349	28.6360	.035	1.0006
89°	.9998	.0175	57.2900	.018	1.0001
90°	1.0000	.0000	∞	.000	1.0000

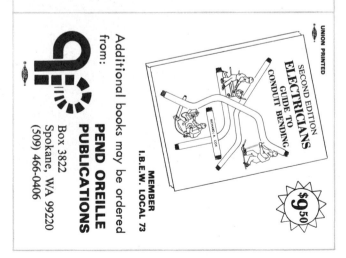
Cut out and fold for wallet sized reference guide.

OFFSET MULTIPLIER (Page 20 = cosecant of the offset angle
offset multiplier X height of obstruction = spacing between bend marks

OFFSET SHRINK PER INCH OF RISE (Page 29)
Subtract the cotagent from the cosecant for the angle of offset and
convert to fraction equivalent.

OFFSET LOCATION MULTIPLIER (Page 28) = Cotangent of the angle
Used to preposition offsets Method #1

PARALLEL OFFSETS ADJUSTMENT (Page 33) = Center to center spacing
X tangent of ½ the
offset angle.

3 BEND SADDLE
Hand Bending (Page 41) A-B, A-C = 2½ X height of obstruction

"CHICAGO" Benders (Page 69) A-B, A-C = 3 X height of obstruction

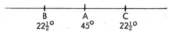

B   A   C
22½°   45°   22½°

OFFSET CONSTANTS FOR PRE-POSITIONING METHOD #1
(Page 23) These values may be used for hand or "CHICAGO" Bender's

	EMT Pipe Size			Rigid Pipe Size		
ANGLE	1/2"	3/4"	1"	1/2"	3/4"	1"
45°	5"	6-1/4"	7-1/2"	5"	6"	8"
30°	4-1/2"	5-1/2"	6"	4-1/2"	5-1/2"	6-1/2"
22-1/2°	3-1/2"	4-1/4"	4-3/4"	4"	5"	6"
10°	3"	3-1/2"	4"	3"	3-1/2"	4-1/2"

Shrink Values for pre-positioning offsets Method #2 (Page 29)

angle of offset	5°	10°	22½°	30°	45°	60°
shrink per inch of rise	1/32	1/16	3/16	1/4	3/8	1/2

SEGMENT BENDING (Page 73)

Developed length = desired radius X 1.57

Start mark = desired stub length – (radius + OD)

Spacing between shots = $\dfrac{\text{developed length}}{\text{number of shots}}$

For smooth radius bends, not less than 3° nor
more than 5° per shot. This rule does not
apply for segment offsets.